# BEAMING D

A Marc John Book

MJ Books

MJ Books
26 Granville Street
Aylesbury
Buckinghamshire, HP20 2JR

Published by MJ Books 2005
Copyright © Marc John 2005

*A catalogue record of this book is available from
the British Library*

ISBN 0-9549040-0-1

Printed and bound in Great Britain by
Antony Rowe Ltd, Chippenham

*Dedicated to all the artists out there*

# CONTENTS

INTRODUCTION . . . . . . . . . . . . . . . . . . . . . . . . . . . . . . . . . . . . 1

1.  A NEW GAME IN TOWN . . . . . . . . . . . . . . . . . . . . . . . . . . 3

2.  YONDER ZONES . . . . . . . . . . . . . . . . . . . . . . . . . . . . . . . .27

3.  THE PENDULUM SWINGS . . . . . . . . . . . . . . . . . . . . . . .49

4.  ONE REVOLUTION AT A TIME . . . . . . . . . . . . . . . . . . .75

5.  SLINGS AND ARROWS . . . . . . . . . . . . . . . . . . . . . . . . . 103

6.  THE HI-TECH GODS . . . . . . . . . . . . . . . . . . . . . . . . . . . 129

7.  THE MACHINE . . . . . . . . . . . . . . . . . . . . . . . . . . . . . . . 151

8.  ALL HIS POWERS . . . . . . . . . . . . . . . . . . . . . . . . . . . . . 177

9.  IT AIN'T OVER YET . . . . . . . . . . . . . . . . . . . . . . . . . . . . 207

10.  THE STARDUST SETTLES . . . . . . . . . . . . . . . . . . . . . . 235

# INTRODUCTION

I would like to introduce this book as though I'm at the stage where I've just taken the call from New York confirming that David Bowie has said yes to the idea. You'll understand the context better in due course.

I'm some piece of work! I've just bagged a superstar and the world is about to start turning just a little bit differently now as I set everything into motion. Nobody but me could have made this happen. I'm so damn good at this I should hit the lecture circuit at some point and play the scholarly master!

It was a tough pitch initially, with marketing directors switching off whenever anything overly technical was worked into the discussion. But you can't keep a good gadget down. And all the technology wanted was somebody to explain it, promote it and bring it to the fore so it could work its magic.

The digital revolution that swept across the world at the beginning of the 21st century couldn't help being impersonal. But it found a friend in me, for sure. Now it's found a friend in a certain pop legend too. Oh boy, it's really going to take off now and feel like we're all being swept along by something far greater than any, single one of us!

I won't put a foot wrong. It'll be a masterful display of ingenuity. When I'm through with this the whole world will know I've really arrived on the scene. Doubters are welcome. Rivals beware. There's just no stopping me. Do you realise who I am?

# A NEW GAME IN TOWN

I was upstairs in the EasyInternetCafé on Tottenham Court Road in London about to take a conference call with two of David Bowie's publicists, one of whom was in New York and the other who was probably just around the corner. This PR company, The Outside Organisation, was apparently a very big player in the music industry and if they got behind something the chances were it would happen. I had a big idea for them to consider on behalf of their legendary star and my pitch had to be perfect because these were not the type of men you could get on the telephone any time you felt like it.

Also on the line from New York was Julie Borchard, the Senior Vice President for International Marketing at Sony Music Entertainment, Bowie's record label. Julie was already sold on the big idea and had been an invaluable and powerful ally in taking it as far as it had come. It was June of 2003 and if all went according to plan it was going to be a Kodak year, one for the career album. Mine was still a young career, maturing like a flower in need of the sunshine that stars like David Bowie can bestow upon it.

As we waited for Bowie's publicists, David Whitehead in New York and Julian Stockton in London, to join us on the call I tried to keep my deep breathing quiet. I was nervous and this was a relaxation technique that, ironically, I was working too hard to get right. I didn't usually get nervous. I thought nobody could make me nervous any more and I was even silently embarrassed. I wondered what was wrong with me, was I going weak and losing whatever edge had got me there in the first

place? I couldn't tell if Julie was nervous, if she was taking deep
breaths too she was keeping them quieter than mine!

Julian Stockton came on the line first and had a friendly chirp
to his voice which put me at ease somewhat. All Julian knew so
far from Julie was that I was some gung ho "new media" type
from Odeon, the UK's largest cinema chain, who had an
interesting remit to develop new business by programming live
events on cinema screens using satellite equipment and digital
projectors. I felt excruciatingly baited to launch into my pitch
right away because, being all coiled up with nerves, I just wanted
to get it over with. But we had to wait for David Whitehead in
New York to join us and while the seconds ticked by like hours I
was forced to ply the art of small talk instead.

Fortunately Julie filled in a lot, having all sorts of things to
tell Julian in general about Sony's forthcoming marketing
campaign for David Bowie's then new album, titled *Reality,*
which was due out in September 2003. With my mobile phone
pressed hard against my ear to block out the chatter in the
background the one thing I didn't want to tell anyone was that
we were actually running out of time to make a David Bowie
cinema gig happen. This conference call was vital, like a final
audition where the role had to be nailed. The chit-chat rolled
annoyingly on. Where was David Whitehead? I could barely
stand it anymore!

"Why don't you go ahead and start, Marc," Julian finally
said.

I think I winced. If there was one thing that didn't agree with
me it was hitting the verbal gas pedal to go roaring off down the
track only to have to hit the brakes and back up to collect a late
arriving passenger. But the moment had come to speak up, to
take command of the call and do justice to the fact that I was on
the telephone with these people in the first place. I drew my last
deep breath and silently reminded myself that I had pitched this
idea almost a hundred times before so all I needed to do was
relax and do it again ...

Nine months earlier I had been knocking on the doors of
every major record label in London trying to get my big idea
through the door but nobody really grasped the potential until I

got around to Sony Music. A meeting was arranged and sometime in October 2002 I went along to their London offices in Great Marlborough Street, where I had to stop myself before going inside to wrestle off my Italian pure silk tie and unfasten the top two buttons of my crisply pressed Burberry shirt. The jeans and sneakers brigade going in and out of the building made it obvious that they didn't do suits and ties much in the record industry and suddenly I felt pretentious and stuffy. I ruffled my neatly combed, side-parted hair and checked myself in the reflection of the glass wall. I still looked too serious and tried cocking a nice, laid back smile, then whistled some catchy pop tune to get me even more into the right spirit as I headed inside.

I was there to tell their marketing managers about something called "digital cinema" and how it was creating new opportunities for the music industry that had never existed before. The pitch was simple. For over 100 years cinemas worldwide had relied on mechanical film reel projectors to show movies produced on film negative. These movies arrived at the cinemas in big, circular canisters, were fed through film projectors and then shipped back to the film companies after their run had finished.

But the digital age had started to change all that. At the turn of the 21st-century cinemas had begun to experiment with digital projectors to show movies and other media that could be stored on powerful computer hard drives or broadcast live by either satellite or fibre cable. This had the potential to radically transform the nature of programming available to movie audiences and blew the doors wide open for new concepts such as live music, sport, video games and all manner of digital programming to reach and revolutionise the cinema screen. Hollywood may have owned the silver screen throughout the 20th century by virtue of dominating the production supply chain and distribution channels for feature films but the age of digital cinema was ripe for pioneers and new visions.

That's where I came in. I had made digital cinema my specialty and, especially, the programming of "alternative content" such as that described. I wanted to build a New

Hollywood the same way the phenomena of the Internet had built a New Economy and my Odeon brief had given me exactly that opportunity! The key to all this, of course, was explaining the concept of digital cinema to companies who lacked any understanding whatsoever about either the cinema business or digital technology – and then convincing them of its potential to generate new revenues and benefit them in ways they would never have considered before. It was Sony Music's turn that day to listen to a digital evangelist preaching the merits of conversion!

The music industry had already come face to face with digital by then, having been severely walloped by illegal music downloading on the Internet. Facing millions of dollars of lost revenues the music industry was suffering a worldwide crisis and, at the outset of this contagious epidemic of societal misbehaviour, record industry chiefs were slow to make fire with the digital sticks; instead wanting them tossed into a river to float irretrievably away. But, eventually, the once clever people in the music business got clever again. They had started listening to people with something to say about digital and I came along at just the right time. A year earlier and they might have seen me just to facilitate my assassination. A year later and somebody else would have been filling my shoes already. Timing is everything. So there I was, still looking far too slick but nevertheless psyched up and ready, to tell the music mafia there was a new game in town.

In the elevator riding up to the fourth floor, where the power brokers at Sony Music were gathering in readiness for me to justify taking up their precious time, it never ceased to amaze me that I was about to hand out business cards relating to a business I never actually planned as a career for myself. I had occupied the position of Head of Digital Cinema for just over ten months, having signed a lucrative two year contract with Odeon in January of 2002 which included a healthy percentage of any sponsorship deals that were made on digital programmes I was responsible for. Before that I was a broke, struggling, low budget moviemaker who wanted to change the world by making socially conscious movies.

In the summer of 2000 I shot a feature length movie on digital
video cameras for just under £10,000 called *Jesus the Curry King*
which I had aspirations to show in cinemas around the world. In
January of 2001 I showed the movie to Odeon executives in the
plush Princess Anne screening room of the BAFTA headquarters in Piccadilly, London, using a digital projector and a
digital tape player that BAFTA had installed alongside a
traditional 35mm film projector. My hope was that Odeon
would like it and agree to book it nationwide and that this
would help me clinch exhibition deals elsewhere in Europe and
America.

I had pitched the movie to Odeon as being ideal for their
student locations such as Leicester, Leeds, Liverpool and
Brighton, among others, and the Odeon film bookings chief
Tony Giddings had been encouragingly open minded about
considering a low budget independent movie across those sites.
Tony preliminarily agreed that, if the material met Odeon's
customary, minimum quality level in terms of its audio and
visual presentation and that if the content itself could not be
considered offensive or objectionable, then they were quite
prepared to offer it a one-week release across maybe a dozen of
their best student-oriented sites nationwide.

Tony Giddings and some other Odeon people duly came
along to BAFTA and sat through my 94–minute guerrilla effort
and I was pleased to see them all leave at the end rather than
sneak out in the middle. I was even more pleased to get a call a
week later from Tony's secretary saying that he would be happy
to set up a meeting with me to discuss the distribution of *Jesus
the Curry King*. My spirits soared as though jettisoned into outer
space. All my dreams about being a first time director whose
little movie defied the odds and made it onto the big screen
suddenly smelled within tasting distance!

However, there was just one little problem. In the meeting
with Tony, at Odeon's headquarters in London's Leicester
Square, he told me that I would have to supply the movie on
35mm film reels and not on digital tape. What? Why couldn't I
simply send out DVD discs for the movie to run on DVD
players through digital projectors, similar to what I had done at

BAFTA? This, after all, was what I was expecting and was within my limited, dwindling budget. Tony explained that Odeon – and cinemas in general – had yet to convert to digital projection and that all of its film releases were shown on 35mm film reels. BAFTA, he explained, had a digital projector because they showed a lot of video presentations. Odeon, simply put, did not have a nationwide network of digital projectors and if I wanted to distribute my movie I would have to convert my digital tape to film negative and send out reels.

A tape-to-film conversion was never going to be viable for me. Film is expensive and this is why digital moviemaking was seen as such a liberating force for new directors in the first place. Transferring 94 minutes of digital picture and sound onto 35mm film negative was going to cost around £500 per minute plus duplications. In other words if American Express were happy to increase my credit limit by around £50,000 then it wouldn't be a problem. Except there was more chance of a money tree sprouting up in the Gobi desert than American Express or any of my other numerous creditors letting me borrow a penny more.

Finding, borrowing, stealing or winning a Vegas jackpot to the tune of £50,000 was simply out of the question and it seemed cruelly ironic that the digital tools of the future that had brought me so close to the brink of securing a theatrical release were being repelled by the archaic 19th century film technology it would ultimately replace. It was as though film technology itself took on the shape of an ugly, antiquated gargoyle making a grumpy, defiant statement that it didn't want things to change in the world and that digital urchins like me could go right back to wherever we came from.

On the spur of the moment I put it to Tony that perhaps another option could be for *me* to temporarily supply the digital projectors. Tony scratched his head for a few moments as though activating a vital portion of his brain to process a response and slowly his eyeballs were fed a view on the idea. Finally he said that provided there were no technical costs or insurance liability to Odeon then, yes, it would be fine for me to supply the digital projectors and show my movie the way it had been shown at BAFTA. I asked Tony to give me a week to check into the feasibility of this and he was fine about that, appreciating that my spontaneous thinking needed some fleshing out. I didn't know how expensive digital projectors were but I didn't imagine they were cheap. And I needed mine for a whole week across maybe a dozen locations! I could have felt utterly despondent and defeated but strangely I didn't ...

As the elevator doors parted to bring me out onto the fourth floor of the Sony Music building I snapped my mind back to the moment at hand. It was time to get in the *zone*, that place of disciplined concentration that a professional in any results-driven field depends on for optimum performance. A pretty secretary showed me into a large corner office where I rested my weighty laptop case on a circular table around which I guessed the meeting would be convened. I then straightened my back to shake the hands of the people who were already gathered, which included UK marketing directors Dave MacGregor and Tim Frasier-Harding, the boss woman Julie Borchard and a consultant to Sony Music named Robert Young. It was an eclectic mix of accents, since Dave was from Australia, Tim from England, Julie from America and Robert from Ireland! This was the first time I had met any of them after initially striking up a dialogue with Robert Young, who had been the person to reply to an email pitch I had sent to Sony Music about a month earlier.

As we were in the final quarter of the year I knew the marketing budgets of most record labels for the following year's album launches were probably not yet fully appropriated and I wanted to get something on the ball for 2003. I had yet to deliver any live events and music concerts were seen as the obvious premium content to target.

As teas and coffees were being brought in and rested onto the clear glass surface of the circular table I flipped open my laptop and powered up. I began my slide presentation with bullet points outlining what digital cinema was in terms of the basic technology. The easiest way to describe the technology was to say it differed very little from the proven solutions used in digital TV broadcasting. The same satellites in space that were transmitting multi-channel digital television to homes could just as easily carry programmes to cinemas and the only modification required would be to use a higher rate of compression for the picture.

Compression was easy for everyone to understand and involved how much a data file is condensed in order to transfer it from one point to another. Satellite TV programmes are heavily compressed but the picture at the end is perfectly fine considering the size of the average TV screen. However, if you tried displaying a picture compressed for digital TV on a typical cinema screen, which can measure up to ten metres in diameter and over, the quality would struggle and suffer all sorts of glaring artefacts from patchy pixel loss to blurred images. But by simply increasing the compression rate to allow the programme to pass through what amounts to a much fatter broadcasting "pipe" you can achieve what we might call "big TV" in cinemas, where the image quality has been suitably upgraded to look as clear and sharp as it would on a normal sized TV.

It took me less than three minutes to summarise this basic, technological fact and the Sony folks grasped it with all the ease of an astute class of able students. I continued the lesson.

At home the digital TV programmes pass through decoder boxes which connect to the back of our television sets via any number of leads. These programmes will typically have been encrypted before transmission in order that only subscribing customers can watch them, and these decoder boxes serve the primary function of decrypting the scrambled picture prior to routing the signal to the TV screen. This process applied to cinema broadcasts as well, I explained, with slightly higher grade, professional decoder boxes receiving and decrypting the signal upon arrival. But with a cinema broadcast, instead of the decoder box being connected to the back of a TV set it would be connected to a digital projector which, in turn, would shoot the image out onto the cinema screen with the aid of powerful image processing.

I touched on the ability to play out live digital 5.1 surround-sound as well, which I explained had never been done before in a cinema, and could sense they were particularly keen on this aspect of the technology. I might have overlooked the importance of sound but for the fact that, having worked with Dolby in the past, they had ingrained into me to never forget that sound is actually *half* the experience an audience has in a cinema. With a music event the sound would probably account for *more* than half the experience and this certainly wasn't lost on Sony.

So far I had been describing the technical link-ups for live cinema broadcasts so I clarified that for non-live music DVDs or anything pre-recorded the material could feed into a digital projector from a normal DVD player or run off any computer hard drive. The technical entrails could get a lot more specific than that but they didn't need to know any more about the engineering side than the average man in the street needed to know how the finite components of a TV worked. Simply put, digital cinema worked when you switched it on and the technology behind it wasn't rocket science.

Since these proven methods of compression, encryption and transmission were already well established and operational 24/7 throughout the digital TV world the most significant catalyst in advancing digital cinema had been the electronic projectors. It wasn't until the late 1990s that advances in digital projection had reached a level of image reproduction capable of doing a full range of video formats justice on a cinema screen. Until then the well aged image quality of film negative and its reliable, mechanical means of projection had been the untouchable, superior and exclusive "technology" in the big screen exhibition business.

We all sipped our drinks and the absence of questions told me that the deepening technical references had not yet found any of them feeling intellectually challenged, so I continued to steadily move the slide presentation along.

Hollywood had not been ignorant of the progress made with digital cinema and, indeed, had a lot to gain from cinemas migrating to the new technology, not least the tremendous amounts of money they would save from not having to create and ship thousands of 35mm film reels around the world every time they released a new movie. With satellite or fibre channel distribution they could transmit an entire movie file to tens of thousands of theatres simultaneously at the push of a button, working from just a single master version. And if they still preferred hard media they could always courier discs for play-out on local cinema servers and still slash costs by enormous margins. The estimated savings of digital distribution, whether through satellite transmission, underground fibre or by hard disc, was purported to be worth around $1.5 billion annually to the Hollywood film studios when compared to the old system of striking film prints and having their bulk physically shipped and collected.

What stopped digital cinema from experiencing its own Big Bang and reinventing the worldwide exhibition industry over-night were, quite simply, the politics at work in Hollywood over how it should all best function. Hollywood was not happy with digital TV solutions for the compression, encryption and transmission of files, for example. Hollywood was not happy with the hardware or software proposed for showing movies off hard discs on custom built servers. Hollywood was not even happy with the upper scale of digital projection on offer, despite most people preferring the digital image to its film counterpart in comparison tests. Most of all the Hollywood studios were not happy with the idea that they should fund digital installations instead of the exhibitor, despite the fact that it was Hollywood who would primarily benefit from a financial point of view.

All of these factors combined to make digital cinema certainly a very hot potato but one that was still half baked and nowhere near being taken out of the oven – at least as far as Hollywood was concerned. But numerous exhibitors in America and Europe were not going to wait for Hollywood to pass judgement on technical standards or come up with a third party financing solution and, instead, were quite prepared to put their own money into some of the younger technology models in the hope of generating a diverse range of programming that would be altogether new and different from the supply of film coming out of Los Angeles.

Already during 2002 experiments in broadcasting live pop concerts to cinemas had been undertaken, although I hadn't been involved in any of them and neither had Odeon. Nevertheless, two significant proofs of the concept had been demonstrated and, despite both being on fairly limited scales, these early successes could not be denied. The first of these featured the America rock band Korn who, on June 10th, performed their new album at the time, *Untouchables,* live at the Hammerstein Ballroom in New York with the concert being broadcast simultaneously to thirty-seven movie theatres across the US. Just a few months later, on September 18th, Bon Jovi performed their new album *Bounce* at the Shepherds Bush Empire in London and the show was beamed live to fourteen cinemas, eleven in the UK and three in Germany. Nobody had yet done a global event, though, and such a feat was quickly assuming a landmark status of moon landing proportions, so a great deal of innovation and market leadership were still up for grabs.

I proceeded to describe my grand vision of a Sony Music artist or band performing the world's first live and interactive pop concert beamed via satellite exclusively to cinemas around the world, where song requests could be taken live from randomly selected fans in dozens of countries and that even a question and answer session could be done. It would make history and score huge PR, just what an album launch would want! It was a decent pitch, I was perfectly in the zone throughout and was able to sit back comfortably at the end of it and let their eyeballs linger on the final 'Thank You' slide of my laptop presentation and digest the scope of it in their own time. After a few moments the slightest of smiles broke across Julie's face and it seemed that maybe I was on the brink of a breakthrough.

Bowie's name first came up as a candidate for the big screen treatment at EMI Music actually, who apparently happened to own his entire back catalogue. In December 2002, not long after first seeing Sony, I went along to meet Andy Melchior, EMI Music's Head of New Media at the time, who liked the idea enough to try getting it off the ground as a marketing ploy for the March 2003 DVD release of *Ziggy Stardust and the Spiders from Mars*, except the word came back that Bowie was less inclined to do special promotions for material that wasn't new.

Early in the spring of 2003 David Bowie's name came up again, this time from Sony Music, who had decided the idea might work as part of the launch for his next album. I crossed my fingers. It had been bitterly disappointing that the dialogue with EMI hadn't progressed because David Bowie was exactly the kind of star the concept needed to take off. Bowie was known to spot the next big thing before it was the next big anything. In the 1980s he was one of the first artists to use e-mail to communicate with the media while on tour and, in the 1990s, he was also among the first major music stars to offer fans the chance to download his latest release from the Internet, in the first widespread use of the technology. If a visionary trendsetter like Bowie said yes to the idea it wouldn't be a case of getting a cat in the bag but the king of the beasts himself!

Nine months later there I was in the EasyInternetCafe along Tottenham Court Road with my cell phone pressed hard against my ear as I once again reeled off my abridged history of cinema in the context of the digital revolution. With Julie Borchard, Julian Stockton and finally David Whitehead huddled on the call I laid out the whole glorious spectacle and how I could make it work.

"What happens if the satellite goes down?" David asked.

I was tempted to make a joke about running for cover except you wouldn't know where to run to. But I stuck to sounding bland and convincing because smart asses usually end up on them. The chances of a highly sophisticated, million dollar piece of orbital engineering suddenly dropping from the stars – and choosing the two hours during our proposed Bowie event to do it – was extremely unlikely and I think everyone on the call knew that. But Whitehead's worry was obviously about technical failure in general, especially since we were talking about a live satellite transmission across the entire globe.

"Live TV goes out across the world," I countered, "think about award shows like the Oscars and sports events like the Super Bowl. This would be no different except the live feed goes to cinemas instead of homes."

I didn't get into the fact that possibly up to six satellites would be needed to succeed in bouncing the signal around the globe given that no single satellite had a global footprint. It wasn't especially relevant right then and may only have increased the blood pressure of anyone genuinely worried about gargantuan satellites hovering above the earth catastrophically malfunctioning. It made for a neat movie idea though. I could well imagine an epic disaster tale crammed with spectacular special effects where these truly awesome metal structures plummet to earth with all the fury of an alien bombardment, followed by the public chaos that would follow from most of the world's telecommunications and TV coverage being knocked out!

I couldn't pretend the organisational challenge wasn't vast but I honestly didn't feel it was beyond my management, plus I had some prior successes I could point to already although nothing quite as big. The previous year I had organised a special satellite relay of live World Cup football from Japan and North Korea to a half a dozen Odeon cinemas up and down the UK using similar solutions to what I was proposing now. I had taken the off-air TV feed at BT Tower and had a higher compression signal of the picture sent to temporarily installed satellite dishes and video projectors at the cinemas, proving in practice the principle of increased compression working on a cinema screen.

As it happened the chaps from Outside knew someone who had gone to Odeon Leicester Square to watch one of the matches and enjoyed the experience. This boosted my currency as a technical facilitator as well as affirming that audiences really were prepared to come to a cinema to watch something other than a movie. Whitehead and Stockton said they would take the idea to Bowie along with their personal views but that the final decision would come from the man himself. I suppose that was all I could ask for and the call ended positively enough.

After all my business meetings or important calls I liked to tuck myself away in a little coffee shop somewhere to analyse my performance and thrash through everything said and unsaid. The main check points of my self-examination were how well or not I did simplifying the technology and whether the benefits had been sufficiently expressed. I could be ruthlessly self-critical if I felt my powers of articulation had failed me and sometimes my post-meeting dissection could be horribly masochistic.

As I came out onto Tottenham Court Road and headed down Oxford Street I had already started to mentally replay my presentation of the technical facts and the pitch overall. I had some cause to feel upbeat considering that I had been the most technically illiterate person in the world just eighteen months prior. When I left the meeting with Odeon film bookings chief Tony Giddings in January 2001, faced with the challenge of having to supply a dozen digital projectors or else resign my movie to VHS book shelf status, I didn't even know what a digital projector looked like, much less how anything digital actually worked.

Back then, as a fledgling moviemaker with no prior experience in any audio or visual medium, it had been a triumph simply to master the settings on a digital video camcorder and the idea that I might one day give a beginner's class on global satellite broadcasts to David Bowie's publicity team would have seemed as alien to me as taking the hand of a red planet native for a foxtrot on Mars! I owed all my acquired technical expertise on the subject of digital cinema to the consequences of that fateful day when Tony Giddings could have been forgiven for thinking that some anonymous, no budget movie dreamer was about to bite the dust. Not me, fella!

As I settled into a steaming café latte in a nice little sandwich shop along Old Compton Road in Soho my thoughts began to drift down the long and winding road that had brought me to where I now was in my life. My movie *Jesus the Curry King* first came to life back in April of 2000, when I woke up one morning deciding I was going to make an independent movie and get it shown in cinemas no matter what it took. I was inspired by how a low budget American movie shot on digital video camcorders called *The Blair Witch Project* had made its way to cinema screens around the world just a year earlier and believed I could follow its example.

Digital video, or DV as it was better known, had created something of a revolution in the low budget independent film world by the late 1990s. Digital camcorders were cheap, the quality was excellent and the conditions under which DV could be shot were far more flexible than film. DV was also hip. It had a guerrilla feel to it and there was nothing discreditable about shooting a micro-budget DV movie. Even the mainstream film magazines were beginning to comment on the new styles and opportunities the digital age would create. Of course, not everyone with a DV camera was going to be a David Lean or a Steven Spielberg but anyone out there with real potential was going to find moviemaking a lot more accessible thanks to DV.

*The Blair Witch Project* was not the only DV movie flying a flag of respectability for the medium. A Dutch DV *auteur* named Lars von Trier had been making headlines as well with numerous critical successes on the festival circuit across Europe at about the same time. Von Trier had a highly stylistic approach that utilised the format's advantages to the maximum, which mainly incorporated an exclusively hand-held shooting style as well as using entirely natural sound and light, all of which he popularised as the "dogma" approach to digital moviemaking.

Such experimentalism and ingenuity were giving the new medium a freshness and visual signature that made it no fleeting novelty. For under £500 you could own an excellent DV camera, shoot a full length movie, edit it at home on a PC and even stand a chance of getting it shown in cinemas, as *Blair Witch* and Mr von Trier had proved – even though I didn't realise at that point that the tape-to-film divide would ultimately still need to be crossed.

Nevertheless, DV technology and the liberation it promised new directors around the world was here to stay and DV movies were only going to get better and bigger. Those fluorescently bright creators behind *The Blair Witch Project* went even further with their innovative grasp of the new, technological era by using the Internet in an unprecedented manner to promote their movie and build an online following. A lot of the movie's success was attributed to the Internet marketing campaign and this was even credited with waking Hollywood up to the viability of online marketing. It was amazing stuff and I decided it was my turn next to get a piece of the revolution.

Indeed, I wanted to make a movie that would actually start a revolution and change the world! I was serious. I wanted to tell a story that said something about what I saw as the three most important things in life – love, spirituality and politics. It was an unlikely trio of themes, the blending of which would be far from anyone's first choice formula for a hit movie, but I had special reasons for feeling they belonged in a film.

For me every story starts with a character, so I started thinking about what kind of character could have something to say about love, spirituality and politics without an audience feeling that such a character was unpalatable. Only one character came to mind. I decided I was going to make a movie about the second coming of Jesus Christ and what his experience in the modern day world might be.

I wasn't a follower of Christianity and had no religious background but I did believe a philosopher and man of charity called Jesus had once walked the earth, so the idea to resurrect him in a modern day setting seemed the perfect scenario for the themes of love, politics and spirituality to find a means of expression that could be relevant to contemporary issues.

The story I came up with involved an ordinary man who wakes up from a coma believing he has been filled with the mind and spirit of Jesus. Seeing that hate, racism and social inequality still plagues the world he takes a job in a local Indian restaurant to show how different cultures can work together and then his cooking recipes start to miraculously transform local bigots – leading people to wonder if he really is the Messiah ...

The movie was all I cared about. Playing around with digital projectors was just a necessary distraction. The special reasons I had for believing that the themes of love, spirituality and politics were the most important considerations to have in life evolved during a process that came before all this. And the way in which David Bowie would soon take centre stage in my life – as well as the significance he would ultimately play in inspiring this story – cannot be properly understood without knowing what that process was ...

It really all started with a dream, not one in sleep but the kind young people have about what they want to be when they grow up. I started chasing one dream or another from the moment I first developed an active imagination and it is clear now that I was never going to achieve anything the traditional way, such as learning a trade or working up a career ladder. Instead I was the kind of dreamer who would always depend on taking long shots in the hope of achieving some spectacular, improbable success.

The first thing I remember wanting to be with any true conviction in my life was a writer. That was my dream. I wanted to become a writer from the age of eleven, ever since my English literature school teacher declared there would be a class competition to find out who could write the best, fictional story, with the prize being that the winning story would be read aloud by the teacher and then displayed on the classroom wall for all to admire.

At school I was one of those distant pupils that teachers give up on but I was lucky enough to be a prolific daydreamer and this saved the daily chore from being a total waste of my time. But when that story assignment was given out I suddenly switched on. I must have had the feeling that *writing* might actually be a worthwhile depository for all that daydreaming I was doing and that maybe I should try it. I don't know why it didn't occur to me sooner but on that day something ignited in me that was never there before and I wanted to show the teacher and the whole damn class what an unassuming little superstar I was!

I was determined to write an amazing, sensational and unbeatable story that I titled *Fire,* which was about a hospital that becomes engulfed in a deadly blaze and the hero doctor who risks his life to save his patients, sacrificing himself and perishing in the process to save a young girl at the end.

It had everything my eleven-year-old imagination could conjure up in terms of drama, suspense and "plausible" heroics, which included giving the hero doctor a gymnastics background so he could somersault over menacing walls of flames and cartwheel through tight, blaze-drenched corridors. To be honest I don't remember much more about the detail, except that it was a very long story. For some reason I thought the story had to be very long to be any good.

We all handed in our stories at the end of the class for the teacher to take home and judge and I could barely wait for the following week's class when I fully expected my talent to be unveiled before the assembly of my peers. I was so certain it would be the winner I would have bet my lunch money on it.

The teacher hated it. He crossed out each page with a thick red pen and at the end of it simply wrote the word "appalling". He hated my story so much I wondered if he actually hated me too! I couldn't believe it. It took me several minutes staring at each defaced page before I could finally accept that I hadn't won the competition. I felt like crying. It was a good thing I hadn't bet my lunch money!

The world would have been an unforgivable place to endure that day had it not been for one thing – the winning story. The winning story did more to inspire me to become a writer than the competition had in the first place. When the teacher, Mr Wells, announced that a quiet, unassuming and not especially bright kid named Elio Giordano had won I thought at first it was a mistake. Elio was a friend of mine. His father drove the local ice cream van around our neighbourhood and whenever I would be at Elio's house playing games we would often raid the confectionary supply. I think this explained why Elio was slightly overweight and why I suffered too many trips to the dentist. Whatever the case, Elio was the last kid in the class I expected to win the competition. Nothing in his speech, personality or general character suggested he had the imagination or interest in storytelling to write the winning story.

Elio's story was titled *Stop Thief* and told the tale of a bank heist where the getaway was made by helicopter from the roof of the bank. This meant the police had to deploy their Special Air Alert Team to take up pursuit. This resulted in a fantastic chase across the skies which was brilliantly conceived and written. The images Elio had conjured up describing the high powered police planes, equipped with laser rifles and turbo boosters, was mesmerising.

By the end of Mr Wells reading *Stop Thief* aloud to an utterly compelled and awed class I had forgotten the grief of not winning. Instead I was filled with an appreciation for good storytelling that I never had before and I was awash with fresh inspiration to try again – but not in school. I switched off again once that teacher trashed what had been a vital awakening in my young mind and went back to daydreaming, writing only when I got home. The most ironic thing to remember now is how teachers would tell me to stop daydreaming without ever realising that this was the one and only thing capable of saving me from a life barren of passion and purpose. Bless all the young rebels!

My other passion was watching movies and I loved them from an early age, even more than cartoons. I can remember around the age of six or seven the joy of staying up late watching James Cagney re-runs and old, black and white RKO horror classics on the UK's BBC2 channel. Usually they would run past midnight and I would only get to watch them because my mother would invariably fall asleep around ten o'clock, hence I wouldn't be sent to bed before they finished. Whenever she did stir, notice the time and banish me to my bedroom it was always a source of great consternation. I would fall asleep imagining how they might have ended.

As a young teenager I became fascinated with the history of cinema and started reading non-fiction books on the birth of Hollywood by historians like Kevin Brownlow and David Gill. Legendary trailblazers like Mack Sennett, Samuel Goldwyn, Carl Laemmle and Irving Thalberg captivated me with their great visions and success in building a movie-making empire that still stood at the dawn of the 21st century. Thalberg was my hero. He was the original boy wonder who, in 1922, became the production chief at Universal Pictures at the age of just twenty one!

Not everyone moulds the clay of the human experience on a world level for centuries upon centuries but the advent of cinema saw a chosen few achieve exactly this. I don't know why but their legacies made me want to be someone who changed the world too; although I didn't have a clue back then what I wanted to change or if anything needed changing in the first place! I just felt I wanted to be in the company of those in history whose hands had somehow shaped the clay.

By the age of sixteen I decided I wanted to write movie scripts and be an actor. I still wrote short stories but as a budding writer and lover of movies merging the two seemed natural. I believed that maybe I could define myself as someone who changed the world in some way by becoming one of the world's great movie script writers who also starred in his projects. I didn't know what I would write about to achieve this but I was sure something would occur to me. There was no hurry, I was still only sixteen and decided if I didn't get around to changing the world until I was eighteen or nineteen that would be fine.

Around this time I also joined a local amateur drama club and was cast in numerous roles. I liked acting because no doubt I had succumbed to having a bit of an ego at that age and the attention was always nice. Ego gets criticised but it's a great motivator for action and is probably the best tonic for any under-achiever. The girls in the club were nice too.

Ah, girls! From quite an early age I noticed them. The feeling they gave me would rival anything else that came into my life. I first noticed I had these feelings at school, when I was about seven or eight. I was standing in line outside one of the classroom buildings after a lunch period and happened to look over at another line of school kids about ten metres away. Midway in the line was the most beautiful sight my young eyes had ever seen, a girl my age with shoulder length, wavy light brown hair wearing a pretty dress. I couldn't see the colour of her eyes from that distance but she had a stunning, angelic face that mesmerised me.

Nature being nature there comes a time when all young people realise they are sometimes drawn to each other in ways that differ from being idly curious. At that age I didn't know about love, romance, relationships or anything at all about the reproductive process. All I knew was that I was more than idly curious about this girl and I didn't understand why. Then she happened to look around and caught me staring at her. I wasn't surprised she caught me staring, I was pretty certain my eyes had grown the size of bowling balls and that my height had shot up by at least half a metre! How could she miss me? After a few seconds she looked away but I kept looking at her, waiting for my bowling ball eyes and enhanced growth to entice her eyes again.

After a cruel and agonising period of probably less than ten seconds she finally looked over at me again and then her eyes diverted to her teacher, a kindly woman whose name I remember was Miss Evans, whom she beckoned over. My heart raced with excitement as I could clearly see this angelic creature telling her teacher about a boy she had just noticed. Miss Evans turned and looked over in my direction to single me out. Now they were both looking at me. Miss Evans said something back to this beacon of beauty and then, to my amazement, the teacher started walking toward me.

When Miss Evans reached me and leaned over to fully engage my attention I was flush with expectation. My angel had glimpsed her first ever god of love and had sent a messenger to tell me as much, or so I expected ...

"Your name is Marc isn't it?" Miss Evans inquired.

I nodded, feeling a surge of triumph at the mere fact.

"The girl you seem to be staring at ..." the teacher continued, "has asked me to speak to you ..." the teacher paused, almost awkwardly, "well, she wants you to stop staring, you're *frightening* her."

Oh dear, that wasn't the desired effect! But I had discovered a certain allure and the rejection could not disillusion me. From that day on I chased that mysterious feeling as hard as any dream I would ever pursue.

By the time I rolled off the education assembly line in 1987 at the age of sixteen I started to feel very wary about life in a small town. I grew up in a quaint market town called Aylesbury, roughly fifty miles west of London, where nobody did much except watch gloomy English TV soap operas, which was pretty much the case right across the country. It seemed everybody's sense of identity and self-worth had curiously become interrelated with these soap opera characters, as though the entire British national culture was measured and reflected by the lifestyles and attitudes of these fictional, often working class and uninspiring stereotypes on the small screen.

Unlike the glossy, upbeat soaps from America such as *Dallas*
and *Dynasty* none of the English soaps offered any possibility
that the British public could be a successful people; driving
sports cars, owning big houses or excelling in well paid careers.
No. In England the best you could do in Soap Land was to work
on a market stall and freeze on the job, or work part time in a
quaint corner shop and be thankful for having out of date bread
to take home. If you were lucky you might enjoy the glamour of
serving boozy layabouts in a local pub, where the décor hadn't
changed since the 1950s.

In England the no-hope culture was rife. Success was just a
word in the dictionary and any reference to it in evidence could
usually only be found in American soaps. The national news was
not much better. Strikes, riots, unemployment, crime; all served
up by Brit newsreaders with accents so outrageously "posh" it
almost made one feel intellectually inferior to sound any
different. With probably ninety five percent of the British
population sounding nothing like these pseudo-aristocratic
talking heads I often wondered if creating an inferiority complex
en masse was actually part of the Establishment's agenda to
further subjugate their plebeian ranks!

Yes, I was the quintessential angry young man – fervently
anti-establishment, anti-British, anti-everything. Oh the fun and
joy of being a teenager in 1980's Britain! Out of the mental
labour camp of organised education I came into the class
divisive and terminally pessimistic society of late 20th century
Britain. Margaret Thatcher's Conservative Party ran the
country like contemptuous feudal barons from unassailable
castles in Westminster and to my disgust the peasants across the
land seemed perfectly happy to forget a man like Oliver
Cromwell ever existed. My solution was simple. Get out fast.
So I made the decision I was going to move to America!

My decision to move to America whilst still in my mid-teens
was met with derision and disbelief by everyone around me.
Nobody did such a thing in British soap operas and none of
those Duke of Nothing newsreaders ever reported such a story
so how could I possibly be serious? Surely such a move was
doomed to disappointment, failure and probably even a violent

death! After all, I was a subject of the Crown, a servant of the British Empire, subjects and servants are not supposed to be ambitious, individual and single minded. But I was.

It was around this time that I first felt the curious, compelling impulse often referred to as *instinct*. I think the only thing to be said about instinct is that it does not need to be understood, it just needs to be followed. I had an instinct that leaving Aylesbury and moving to America was the right thing for me to do. I could not explain why, it just felt right. I think some of my friends had bets on how many weeks it would be before I came back, disillusioned or worse. I think some of my family wondered if they would ever see me again. I told them they would, when I was a star! I told them all I would not come back until it was on a private jet with a stretch limo picking me up at the airport.

My anti-establishment sentiments against the British class structure had convinced me that it was pointless for a small town "nobody" from a working class neighbourhood to try to break into the elitist London theatre, film or acting scene. I had grown up watching films like *Rocky* and believed America truly was the Land of Opportunity, devoid of the class bias that I believed might plague any promise I could show in my own country. After all, Sylvester Stallone himself came from humble, outsider beginnings and succeeded on merit and determination. In London I could not imagine a likewise comparison being drawn; certainly none could be held up as examples.

I picked New York City as my first destination mainly because the airfare was cheaper than a ticket to Los Angeles, so my grand plan was to take Broadway by storm as a playwright and then later fulfil my ambitions to be a successful screenwriter and movie star in Los Angeles. This was my big dream now. Somewhere along the way I imagined I would fall in love and change the world. It was unabashedly naïve but naivety, like ego, can sometimes be a great stimulant for action!

But first I needed to get some money together, although having left school with just a single qualification in drama studies meant I wasn't even getting to the interview stage with the majority of better paid jobs that I applied for. Since I wasn't looking for anything permanent I didn't care what I did so I ended up taking a job as a car cleaner for a local, used car dealership. It was definitive dead end work but they paid me decent cash and in a year I was able to save £1,100 which converted to roughly $1,700 at the time. It felt like a fortune to me and I was ready to live the dream, which is really all a dream asks for.

# - 2 -

# YONDER ZONES

On January 3rd 1989, at the age of seventeen, I flew out of London's Heathrow airport like a wide-eyed starling flapping its young wings en route to a horizon it could not see but simply had faith in finding. Seven hours later when the plane disembarked at JFK airport in New York I took my first breath of American air. It was quite late in the evening, around ten o'clock, when the flight arrived and one of the first sights that made an impact on me was a New York cop taking a leak next to me in a toilet in the arrivals concourse. His holstered gun stood out like an exclamation mark as though punctuating the fact that I had just set foot into a whole new world. I had never seen a gun up close before and it made my eyeballs bulge. I remember trying not to stare at it too long in case the cop thought I was staring at something else and arrested me for indecent behaviour!

I spent my first night in Manhattan at the famous Chelsea Hotel on West 23rd Street. I picked that hotel as my first place of shelter because it had a legacy of famous writer guests, such as Mark Twain, William S. Burroughs and the poet Dylan Thomas, whose spirits I hoped would visit me in my sleep and whisper sweet inspiration in my ear. A kindly porter showed me into my $96–a-night room and I kept asking him if the lock on the door was secure, which he kept assuring me it was. Then I was left alone and the reality hit me, I really had done it, I had left England for America without any job, proper accommodation, family or friends to support me.

I was suddenly scared, unsure of myself and in danger of losing my nerve. The ugly face of fear went nose to nose with me

27

and it wasn't a pretty sight! I snapped the light off, dived under the bed covers, and prayed that foreboding face would evaporate in the darkness. I was so afraid of being all alone in a faraway place on that first night that I cried myself to sleep.

Waking up the next day to my first morning in New York was strange, almost as though I had not yet awakened and was only dreaming of being there. Then it hit me again that I really had come to America and I sat bolt upright as though a fire drill had sounded. The room didn't look as unfamiliar as when I had gone to sleep and this simple familiarity eased some of my anxiety. As I washed and picked out my clothes for the day I thought about the instinct that had guided me here. A feeling that strong couldn't be wrong, could it? Once dressed, I looked hard at myself in the bathroom mirror and didn't let my face leave the reflection until my eyes showed some steel. I tried smiling in an effort to raise some of the brazen spirit I had seen the last time I looked in a mirror in England. In the reflection behind me I could almost see all the people back home who doubted me. Their faces weren't just smiling, they were grinning, wanting me to fail!

That morning and afternoon I took to walking into every store along 7th Avenue looking for any kind of work that might be on offer. I also checked out of the Chelsea Hotel after just that first night and moved into the McBurney YMCA which was conveniently located directly across the street and far better priced at just $21 a night. Around the corner, between 23rd and 24th Street on 7th Avenue, there was a men's clothing shop called *Lewis & Clark* which was probably the twentieth place I walked into looking for a job. Previously I had tried a printer's shop, countless delicatessens, bars, restaurants – you name it!

I told the owner of *Lewis & Clarke* I was looking for work and was a reliable person to employ and to my amazement they hired me on the spot! The owner said he'd pay me $188 a week and I'd get discount too! He even preferred to keep me off the books and pay me cash which was perfect given that my tourist visa status in the country meant that, strictly speaking, I couldn't legally gain employment. It was miraculous. I had been in America less than twenty four hours and already had the means to support myself!

The work was fairly straightforward, serving customers and keeping the clothes on the racks and shelves neat and tidy. Before long I left the YMCA and moved into the Hotel Lexington on East 23rd Street at the better rate of $90 a week. I had $7-a-day food allowance and even with the weekly hotel bill I still had a little left over for leisure spending.

After about six fast months working at the store news came to me that one of its former employees was looking to rent out one of the rooms in his Chelsea apartment for $60 per week. The boss told him to speak to me and I jumped at it, knowing this would give me a little extra spending money as well as a residence that would feel less transient than a hotel.

I ended up keeping that room in Chelsea and the job at *Lewis & Clarke* for just over a year before even more fortuitous circumstances moved me into a different, more lucrative line of work. One of my roommate's friends was a company director in a major New York real estate company called Gala Realty and over dinner one night I happened to mention I was a fast typist and this friend offered me a typing job at one of his uptown offices. I was honest with him about my tourist visa status but he told me not to worry about it.

My pay jumped to $300 a week and I was paid by cheque despite me not having a bank account or a valid social security number. Gala Realty issued me a cheque cashing card that authorised me to cash my cheques at Citibank and I continued to escape sleepless nights worrying about my status as an illegal alien.

After about two or three months filling in the blanks on tenancy forms and sales agreements the office manager where I was based in the Washington Heights section of New York suggested I study for a realtor's licence, which I did during the summer of 1990, and this enabled me to rent and sell property as well. My life in America was getting better and better. By then I was nineteen. I hadn't changed the world yet but I kept telling myself I could always get around to it by the time I was twenty one!

I eventually moved on from Gala Realty to work with a number of other realtors, handling a variety of different properties from Central Park penthouses in skyscraper complexes to small, charming townhouses nestled along tree lined streets. It was a different planet to small town England. My clients were often high flying corporate executives and business school grads on fat salaries looking for their first New York pad. And they all respected me as an equal. I was succeeding among people who were above my academic station but education and class background never came into it. I was in the America I always believed existed, the place where Stallone had shown you can make your fortune.

It was not long before I moved into my own apartment; a small, cheap but utterly agreeable studio rental on the Upper West Side of Manhattan, located along West 75th Street between Amsterdam and Columbus Avenues. It was a gift from my bosses, via a landlord friend of theirs, as a perk for all my hustling. England could not have felt farther away. My hatred for my past and all things British didn't look like thawing and before long I couldn't imagine myself ever going back. At some stage I wanted to legitimise my living arrangement and become a US citizen.

As it happened, my three-month tourist visa status never held me back from over-staying this period because, as a salesman, I was paid strictly commission and was left to file my own tax returns – which I simply never did. For the entire time I was in the realty business this existed as a loophole for me to work and live without having to extend my visa, apply for citizenship or be accountable to the IRS, who had no record of me in the first place.

Morally speaking I was able to sleep at night because, although strictly speaking I was an illegal alien and not paying taxes, I was hardly committing any hard crimes or posing a threat to the public. After all, I was just a wide-eyed kid chasing a dream and slipping through some cracks along the way that just happened to be there already! Sometimes I thought I must have been the luckiest guy alive, but then I'd remember the instincts I'd followed and knew this was a feeling I just had to keep trusting.

Sometime during 1991 the writer in me must have wondered where I had put its voice and gradually, like a volume fader rotating up the decibel scale, it returned. The nature of my work meant I was not punching a clock. As long as I was closing enough deals it hardly mattered if I worked eighty hours a week or two as far as the office managers were concerned and this afforded me the flexibility to indulge in a kind of bohemian café lifestyle to once again remember that I had dreams of writing great stories and changing the world.

I casually started writing and getting reacquainted with my imagination also made me think about my plans to become an actor, so I began taking classes with a very good teacher called Jerry Brody at a studio on West 4th and Broadway. This brought me into contact with a lot of like-minded, aspiring actors and soon I was beginning to feel like a real up-and-comer.

Around the acting scene I noticed the girls, of course. I had not been shy trying out my English accent on susceptible females around Manhattan's bars but nothing like a serious relationship came my way until I found myself starting a relationship with a girl who later moved in with me for a while. Her name was Denise. Denise was from Michigan in the mid-west and she had the bluest eyes I ever saw. We met in a popular bar on Columbus Avenue on Manhattan's Upper West Side called *Lucy's* when we were both pushing at the counter to get served. Straight away the small talk had potential.

Denise was not part of the theatre scene; she had moved to Manhattan to pursue a career as a buyer in the retail clothing industry and was just as relatively new to the city as me. She was a sweet, sensible girl and the first real girlfriend I ever had. At that stage in my life I couldn't really define what love was other than a mighty fine feeling that you couldn't get enough of. With Denise I had this and we were happy in our relationship for almost two years. I don't know what exactly broke us up and we probably would have lasted longer if we had met ten years later. If you're looking for love you need to be ready for a relationship and probably neither of us were at that time and place in our lives.

So my first, real skirmish with the great feeling left me thinking it could come and go, that love was so wonderful and ubiquitous that it didn't need treating as anything rare. I also dated a few actresses but like me they were happy with life as a blur; which I merely happened to be a part of and vice versa. But around this scene it was cool to feel like a hip, unknown actor who, you never know, might just be the next, big thing to come out of New York. I was at a few parties when maybe fifty guys would fit that bill.

My acting coach Jerry was always encouraging me to audition because even auditioning, he told me, was great experience for an actor. My first audition was for a new, independent play and the readings were held on Broadway's famed 42nd Street at one of its many theatre spaces. To my surprise I got the part and was cast in a good supporting role as an Italian gangster having an affair with the crime lord's moll. The play was called *Crime and Painting* and it was some kind of a spin on *Crime and Punishment*. It had been written by a Russian immigrant who had changed his name to Richard Hamilton and he was also directing. Richard's name by birth was unpronounceable, I remember, but far more *avant garde* sounding, although he loved being called Richard Hamilton and with his thick Russian accent and eccentric body language he was as much a character as anything he had written.

We performed the piece at the Gene Frankel Theatre in Manhattan's arty East Village district over two weeks in September 1992 and it was a great education in how to rehearse and stage a play. The Russian may have been a borderline caricature but he had a good sense of organisation. Nobody got paid, we all did it for the experience and as a showcase for whatever talent we believed we had. Nobody thought the play was very good but we had one heck of a time doing it.

The more I found myself around acting classes, script workshops and just the theatre scene in general, the more I thought I should be taking the initiative and producing my own plays, finding my own voice and just seeing what came of it. I had seen what an unlikely Russian immigrant with just a few thousand dollars to spend had achieved in getting a new play onto the stage before paying audiences and some press attendance. So why couldn't I do the very same thing with my own work?

By then I had been in America nearly four, fast years and hadn't yet got serious about being someone who wanted to write and change the world. I was not overly wealthy but in the context of my living expenses I was certainly building up a comfortable surplus and this meant I could consider funding a modest production at any of Manhattan's well regarded "off-off Broadway" venues. Plays that find their way into the "off-off" vanguard can either mean that an exciting, unknown voice is emerging or that some clown with cash to burn thinks he's Eugene O'Neill. But the beauty of it is that an audience, big time producer or theatre critic won't know until they've been along to check it out.

During the summer of 1993 I wrote a play called *Waking Summer* which told the story of five homeless people in a food shelter who become deeply introspective after the shelter's volunteer group fail to show up with food packages. The homeless characters then find themselves challenged to look within themselves for solutions to their common plight, rather than rely on charity and external support. It was a moralising, crusading sermon on the *power of self* to create change internally.

The inspiration for the play came about one cold afternoon in March of that year when I came across a middle-aged homeless woman crouched outside *Zabars*, a fashionable food bazaar on Manhattan's Upper West Side, which was prime begging space because of the non-stop foot traffic it attracted from the cultured locals. This homeless woman was wrapped in a kind of bright, multi-coloured blanket which had succeeded in catching my eye in the first place and I could see by the lack of change in her empty coffee cup that the day's begging wasn't going too well.

I reached into my pocket to root out some change but found I only had a twenty dollar bill. On a whim I decided I wanted to give her some sense of hope so I shook off my reticence and stuffed the bill firmly in her cup, keeping my eyes on hers as I

did so. There was no reaction. Her eyes were still and lifeless
although her occasional, slight shuffling gave away that she was
not dead.

"There's twenty bucks for you," I said, still wanting her to
register a moment of rare good fortune and sympathy shown by
a fellow human being. "Doesn't that cheer you up?"

Her weary eyes then lifted ever so slightly and fixed solely on
mine in an incredible few moments where it felt like the world
had suddenly shrunk to encompass just her and me. She shook
her head.

"You're the first person all day to give me anything," she said
woefully.

"But twenty bucks, that's pretty good isn't it?" I replied.

"If twenty people had stopped today and given me just a
dollar each it would have meant a lot more," she said, her eyes
dropping from mine as though heavy from the strain of her
reality.

I think it was Leo Tolstoy who wrote "What then shall we
do?" on the matter of saving lost souls whose fates had fallen
into darkness. I think he came to the conclusion that all we can
do is give our own small token wherever possible, to "add your
light to the sum of light" as he is quoted as saying.

And that's all I could do for her. But I understood her point;
she needed *more* people to give *less* than one person trying to do
it all alone. As I walked away I looked back and caught a final
glimpse of that woman through the blur of the *Zabars*
customers criss-crossing between us. She had straightened the
blanket around her to some extent and I could now recognise
exactly what it was. It struck a powerful, ironic metaphor
whether this was her intention or not – I could see she was
wrapped in the *American flag*.

Ever since being a teenager, and feeling that I wanted to
change the world in some way, I had never actually come across
anything that really seemed to need changing. But when my eyes
and mind were opened to the disgrace of letting people suffer
hunger and homelessness I suddenly found something in the
world that needed to change. That is why I wrote the play. And if
it didn't solve the problem overnight it didn't matter, if the world

was still no different afterwards then at least I would have done what I could to add some light to where it was clearly needed. The poster for the play, which I paid a homeless street artist to sketch, wasted no time in declaring a statement; it depicted a worn, forgotten homeless victim wrapped despairingly in a soiled American flag and holding out a cup for change. And change not just of the monetary kind. It was a tribute to that woman.

My plan of action was for the play to attract the interest of a backer to help take it on tour or else to get it staged in a bigger, possibly off-Broadway or Broadway venue. I didn't care if it lost money. It was to be an investment in my own development. For the actors it would be a good showcase for their talents, where they could invite agents and anyone else they liked. I would be inviting agents too, thinking that perhaps an agent who liked it could at least get the script read by a potential backer if none actually came to see it.

I copied the same formula for casting and rehearsing the play as Comrade Richard had for *Crime and Painting*. This meant I advertised a casting call in *Backstage*, the weekly newspaper that was New York's theatre bible, and then rented a small theatre space three times a week for six weeks to rehearse. As the writer, producer and director I decided not to cast myself in it as well. This would have been too burdensome and probably just plain egotistical.

The meaning of the title *Waking Summer* drew a metaphor between the seasons of the year and the *inner seasons* that every individual possesses, such as winter when a person's soul may seem cold and dark and summer when the soul is warmer and brighter. The characters in the play invent this metaphor and try to wake the summer in themselves, for their own good as well as to wake the summer in others. For them, and to my way of thinking, the summer in humanity must have fallen asleep for the terrible plight of homelessness and hunger to be tolerated, giving way to a dark winter in the collective soul of Mankind. I didn't at that point consider myself spiritual but that experience seemed to deconstruct my formerly agnostic attitude and to my surprise I was beginning to consider some kind of spiritual context to our existence.

We ran the play at the Inner Space Theatre on West 27th Street in Manhattan's Chelsea district for five nights in September 1993. I made a deal with the theatre owners for them to keep fifty percent of the box office in return for a special discount on the venue hire. Even though I didn't care about the financial return I at least wanted to keep the initial outlay as modest as possible. The play was fairly well attended and didn't actually lose too much money. Nobody walked out and everybody applauded at the end. Did a big time producer or agent see it? No. Did it make anybody think? Maybe. But I had at least applied the Tolstoy principle and added my light. The best thing about it was that I simply did it, that I acted on conviction.

Just as importantly I had become connected to a feeling of having some kind of soul or spirit for the first time in my life. Religion had held no appeal to me back in England but the idea of us having some kind of spiritual origin and destiny now began to stir me into long, deep meditations on the truth about life, death, God and the universe. The young man I had become wanted to know why I was here in this world and what the point of it all was?

Central Park in the middle of Manhattan became my favourite place to sit and think about the "big questions". The park has two huge, public fields that I especially liked called The Great Lawn and Sheep's Meadow, which sprawl out like huge, green beaches where a lot of New Yorkers can enjoy picnics and relax sun bathing as though on the sands of a shore line. The park itself is an enormous, beautifully cultivated place resembling a giant garden with fields, lakes, woodlands and footpaths everywhere. You can enjoy it for hours and I often would. Amidst this peaceful splendour my mind felt warmly encouraged to contemplate the great mysteries of life, and before long all my cogitation and writing had relocated from the cosy eateries of the Upper West Side to this fantastic environment.

What I liked best about Central Park was that its calm, harmonious power flourished at the very centre of the most bustling, chaotic city in the world as though none of the havoc and strife outside existed. This struck me as a powerful symbolism for how an indomitable spiritual peace could be found at the centre of *oneself* too, no matter what distractions and difficulties might beat against our mortal shell. In any place of great natural beauty nature itself can almost assume its own personality, as though living and breathing beyond its own form and reaching out to connect to us with a language that transcends our own. I can think of sunsets, landscapes and ocean shores at day break that will have had this effect on many of us, creating a feeling of calm and harmony with the time and space we are in. If there was a religion or spiritual philosophy that was helping people to feel this togetherness, not just with nature but with *each other*, I hoped I would find it.

I didn't expect I was only person to ever feel this sense of spiritual oneness or that it was even especially new. Surely it was eternally present and I had just happened to find it in me the way anyone in the world could find it if they looked. When it would rain or be too cold for Central Park I would spend whole afternoons lounging on the customer sofas in the supermarket-sized Barnes & Noble bookstore on the corner of 83rd Street and Broadway, where I would seek out other writers who had connected to this feeling, to see how they had managed to describe it and how it had affected their lives.

I came across authors like the famed eastern mystic Paramahansa Yogananda, whose descriptions of spiritual consciousness were staggering. And I was particularly fascinated by the immense personal and spiritual transformation that the black activist Malcolm X underwent during his short-lived but passionate civil rights campaign during the 1960's.

What especially became clear on those rain swept and windy days inside Barnes & Noble was that countless human beings before me had indeed discovered their spiritual centre and sense of oneness with others. It was encouraging to know I wasn't alone in finding this feeling and that I wasn't imagining it either. But what puzzled me was why these revelations hadn't exploded into the mass consciousness and changed the world yet?

In the case of the yogic masters it seemed their union with the Spirit left them far too sedated to challenge the system, and that their answers to life's problems concentrated too much on insulating the individual in a cosy bubble of bliss rather than inspiring action. Whilst in the case of Malcolm X it had been at the hand of the gun that his crusade was thwarted. Whatever the case, it seemed that the good guys were either always outnumbered by the bad guys or that the good guys became too good for the good of others!

Could being spiritual teach me anything about how to address any of this? I continued to seek out the experiences of others to see if anyone had found something beyond the fundamental feeling of oneness, comforting as it was, that could show a person how to keep their harmony and follow their convictions in a world littered with villains, martyrs and yogis!

From then on I wanted everything I wrote and did to somehow express something meaningful about the two things I had found most resonant in my existence up until then, love and spirituality. And then, toward the end of 1994, I strangely found myself thinking more and more about England. I didn't know why. I hadn't kept myself informed about England or stayed in contact with any old friends but suddenly I felt compelled to go back! Everything about leaving New York and turning my back on my American dream at first seemed crazy. I had great friends in New York, a wonderful apartment and an enviable lifestyle six years in the making. I kept telling myself I was insane but at the same time I couldn't deny that America, for some reason, just didn't feel like the place I needed to be in any more.

Finally in November I decided I was going back. The instinct to do it overrode everything else and I knew well enough by then that instincts must always be followed. Despite seeming a backwards step it felt like the right way forward for the changed person I now was. It didn't matter one bit that I wasn't going back on a private jet as a movie star. At the end of those six years just the sheer experience of *living* made me feel like I had surpassed all my dreams without realising any of them! There had been no failure, only the success of my spiritual self-discovery and expanded perceptions. I felt like I could live anywhere in the world now and always feel at the centre of the universe. It was the strangest feeling of triumph I ever experienced.

Leaving America meant I had to go via Toronto, Canada, because I, of course, had become an illegal alien in America as a result of over-staying my initial 3–month visitor's visa. If I had tried to leave from anywhere in the US the best case scenario would have seen me deported and refused re-entry for a very long time. I had no idea what the worst case scenario would have been but I didn't want to take any chances.

Crossing the border from the US into Canada required only that US citizens show either a driving licence or a US voter registration card. The latter was not a form of picture ID but to get one still meant you had to display picture proof of US citizenship in the first place. This meant I was able to borrow a friend's voter registration card and pass myself off as a US citizen. I showed this at the border crossing and was waved into Canada and onto Toronto without so much as a question. A couple of days later I mailed the voter card back to my buddy in New York and, as I dropped the envelope in the mail box, I thanked another crack in the system for letting me slip by.

In Toronto I found my way to wherever the British consulate or embassy office was at the time, saying that I'd been in Canada less than a week, which was true, and that I'd lost my passport and needed them to verify I was British in order for me to board a plane back to the UK. The officials were sweet as sugar and didn't even question me about it. They simply checked my details at the UK passport office in Peterborough, England, and had a facsimile of my original passport whisked over along with a letter of approval granting my re-entry back to the UK.

I spent a very nice week in Toronto before going back, seizing the chance to explore and enjoy another city. I stayed in a dormitory style youth hostel and had my $700 leather jacket stolen but I wasn't too bothered. In a way losing my coat was almost symbolic of me shedding one skin in preparation for another.

When I returned to England and my home town of Aylesbury on December 5th 1994 I was twenty three years old but felt much older. For certain I was not the same angry young hothead that had vilified all things British as a snarling teenager. My spiritual perspective had helped me reappraise my old, vitriolic rages against the society I once ridiculed and I found myself instead taking the view that people, after all, could not help what their environments moulded them into being. Whether it was overbearing parents, wayward peer pressures or any misguiding, social influences along the way, each of us was merely the product of those influences; not one person but a hybrid of everything that ever made an imprint on our fragile, impressionable psyches.

But *under* that psyche was something else. It had been under my own psyche and was there under the psyches of everyone else too. Sometimes people were feeling it and radiating it and sometimes they weren't, usually because the junk cluttering up their psyche would invariably be blocking the way. With this realisation I was able to tolerate and forgive even the most disagreeable of personalities. In fact it was almost enjoyable being put to the test and finding that nobody's foul mood or ignorance could affect me in the slightest.

Steadied by this perspective, like a pot of boiling water brought down to a gentle simmer, I was able to re-assimilate myself back into British culture like a plane making a perfect, gentle touchdown. Even the dreary news, soap operas and all those self-important politicians could be laughed at now. All the same banality may have been going on as before but I had closed the door to all of it and could live in a kind of blissfully detached amusement. I suppose I was closer to the insular bubble espoused by the yogis than the call to action that Malcolm X had been brave enough to answer. But that suited me fine. I didn't feel compelled to change the world any more. One of the best things about finding my spirituality was that it helped me to live in the world just the way it is.

I moved into a small studio apartment in the town centre and went through a string of meaningless jobs as a kitchen assistant in local restaurants. The most settled work I found was as a kitchen porter at the Equitable Life assurance company head-quarters, a massive office complex famed for being Aylesbury's most notable architectural innovation. The building's exterior was made entirely of blue reflective glass and had a leaning design similar to Italy's leaning tower of Pisa. It was another dead end situation but, just like cleaning cars all those years before, I didn't care. It was just a job. It didn't represent who I really was in the world. Besides, I was more interested in falling in love.

The New Year of 1995 arrived and within a month I met the girl who would become my partner for the next seven years. Her name was Joanne. Joanne was 17 when we met and I was still 23. I was her first real boyfriend and she became the girl I thought I would marry. We met in a local pub when I noticed this long, dark haired raven with a beautiful face, stunning body and irresistible smile perched on a bar stool in-between two of her friends. She caught my stare and I confidently beckoned her over. She confidently held her ground and beckoned that I come over to her instead. I wasn't going to be rude and decline the invitation.

In this incredible girl I found someone who I could share my mind with in ways that helped me look to the future and not just revel in my beloved memories. Back in England I had begun to feel a danger that my journey of self-discovery in America might overshadow everything else I might yet do in the world and exist as the defining period of my entire life. Joanne helped me out of that. Whenever we talked the conversations grew from rivers into oceans in that wonderful way that good conversation can and this gradually helped me simplify many of the complex thoughts that my spiritual experience had provoked.

If I didn't know exactly what love was when I was with Denise in New York I was beginning to understand the great feeling better with Joanne. Unlike with Denise, Joanne and I met at the right time in both our lives. Love is *timing*. I even believed that finding Joanne was the mysterious reason I had been drawn back across the Atlantic in the first place. Inspired by this beautiful young girl I set about developing numerous ideas that tried to do justice to the feelings of love and spirituality that I firmly believed were all that mattered in the world. But there was something else that mattered just as much that I had yet to come into contact with ...

On November 27th 1994, a few weeks before I returned to England from Canada, a billionaire British businessman named Sir James Goldsmith publicly announced his intention to launch a new political party dedicated to campaigning for a British referendum on the country's future with Europe. Goldsmith was saying that the European Union was a dictatorship in the making, that British democracy was under threat and that the people had to resist it to protect our independence. The only way he saw we could do this was to force a national vote on the issue and elect to stay out of a United States of Europe.

Goldsmith declared that his party would field candidates in the 1997 British general election in every seat where the main party candidates had not declared themselves in favour of such a referendum. The aim was to win enough seats in Parliament to push through a Referendum Bill and then disband. Goldsmith called his movement The Referendum Party.

I began researching the issues and found that Goldsmith was not alone in his condemnation of the direction Europe was taking. The issue was splitting the unity of *all* the major political parties in Britain and this was no petulant overreaction on the part of an aloof billionaire. The European Union wanted to become a superpower no less and the scheme couldn't work without merging the sovereign states of Europe into virtually a single country, complete with its own central bureaucracy, single currency, common economic policy, single military force and even its own flag and anthem!

The process required all "member states" to transfer their national independence to an unelected executive-arm based in Brussels called the European Commission, which subsequently proposed legislation that a subservient, pro-Commission assembly called the European Parliament would enact. The age of democracy in Europe was indeed being wound down. Politicians everywhere – from former British party leaders to leading French socialists to staunch German democrats – were basically jumping ship from one political system to another, turning their backs on their home countries and taking up unelected, high ranking positions within the European Union bureaucracy. It was astounding.

The bureaucrats, of course, insisted that it was in each country's best interest to belong to a politically unified Europe, which had ambitions to include anywhere from twenty to thirty countries. If that was really the case, Goldsmith said, let's have a full and proper debate on the whole issue and "let the people decide!" I couldn't argue with that and neither could anyone who truly believed in democracy.

It was at that point I realised that love and spirituality could no longer be the only things worth idealising and that *democracy* is just as vital. Just about everything in everyday life is affected by politics: jobs, taxes, health care, education, transport, law and order, war and peace, you name it. And protecting a system that lets the people decide who manages all these vital affairs has to matter as much as anything.

Goldsmith's pugnacious conviction knocked me into a contest I hadn't even realised was being fought and I had to come out of my bubble, which wasn't merely pricked by this courageous rich man but obliterated to pieces. But this wouldn't be something I could do much about as an unknown writer without a movie credit or published novel to his name. If I was going to add my light to this cause it would mean actually getting involved – so I wrote to Sir James and told him to make me a candidate!

Within a few weeks one of his lieutenants wrote back suggesting I come in to have a preliminary discussion at their offices in London. It turned out that my home town, the constituency of Aylesbury, had yet to select a prospective candidate.

Some time early in 1996 I went along to the Referendum Party HQ to pin my heart to the crusade's sleeve. The party offices were modest, situated in a low-rise and unassuming building in the Westminster area of London. After giving my name at the reception desk and waiting for just a few minutes I was greeted by a middle-aged man with one of those aristocratic British accents that TV news readers used to have in the 1980s, although I didn't hold it against him. This chap, let's call him Mr Willoughby for no other reason than the name suits my memory of him, took me into one of a number of small

interview rooms and we sat across from each other in rather a
formal way.

Willoughby had a copy of my letter in front of him along with
some hand scribbled notes along its margin, which intrigued me.
He started off by explaining what I already knew about the
party, including its aims and the transparent intentions of its
billionaire leader to do nothing more than force a public vote on
a national issue that irrefutably deserved one. It seemed some of
the dogs in the media were rabid with suspicion that Goldsmith
had some other, murky agenda and that the Referendum Party
was just a smoke screen. If that was the case I couldn't see it and
Willoughby was practically preaching to the converted. When
his pause invited a comeback I repeated the sentiments of my
letter and told him I didn't suspect Goldsmith of being anything
other than a man of conviction. We then talked about Europe,
the British government and the process of mounting an election
campaign, which he said would be as formidable and well
organised as anything staged by the mainstream parties. British
politics, he assured me, would never have seen anything like it
before.

After about 45 minutes the meeting concluded with
Willoughby telling me that a regional campaign manager
would be in contact with me on the matter of whether I would
be selected. If I was offered the role it would not, of course, be
a paid position, which I knew already. Campaign expenses
would be paid and a capped election budget would be
allocated across all constituencies but nobody was being told
to give up their day jobs, unless they actually got elected to
Parliament of course. This was all fine with me. I liked
Willoughby – and if it ever turns out that was actually his
name I'll be damned!

About a month later I received a letter from the Referendum
Party's regional campaign manager informing me that the party
wanted to select me as their Prospective Parliamentary
Candidate for my home constituency of Aylesbury. I was elated
and could hardly wait for the battle to commence. Writing could
easily wait. Tolstoy had let it wait; the man had fought in the
Russian army after all. He must have known that the pen is *not*

mightier than the sword but that there is a time and place for each.

I began to spread the word about the Referendum Party to the chefs and sandwich makers in the kitchen where I worked but was often met with puzzled expressions as though somehow they couldn't understand the perfectly enunciated ancient Japanese I was speaking. But I did my best to explain the importance of winning their support and it was useful to deal with their blank expressions and naïve assumptions because I would later come across plenty of this on the larger campaign trail.

But if I thought I had any kind of knack for making a point I was in for some fine tuning regardless. During the summer of 1996 Goldsmith put regional groupings of his Prospective Parliamentary Candidates through a series of campaign "boot camps" which involved professional tuition being given by a squad of specialist consultants in how to present oneself and the party line to the media and public.

The degree of organisation and calibre of training personnel at those boot camps was exceptional. This man Goldsmith knew how to make a clock tick. He was fashioning a major political movement and challenge to the Establishment that was the work of precision human engineering. Sir James didn't attend these training weekends personally but the man's gusto was clearly flowing through all nostrils present!

It was yet another world for me. There we were, disparate strangers forging a sense of trench camaraderie over silver service salmon and sorbet, all of it so civilised yet calculating in how our philosophical bayonets were being sharpened for cold, hard political war. It was the closest I ever came to understanding the process of going into any kind of battle with people who at first mean little to you but soon mean a lot more. It suggested to me that there is no such thing as strangers in the world; only friends and comrades everywhere who don't always have the accident of becoming acquainted with each other.

The British general election on May 1st 1997 was probably the last one contested largely in the world of "old media". Interactive TV polling, armchair SMS pundits, chat room radicals and website propaganda had yet to pop up in the mass consciousness. Back in 1997 it was a good, old fashioned 20th century political campaign where paper leaflets and shoe leather were the tried and tested essentials for any local candidate hoping to reach the hearts and minds of their constituents.

Cynical pundits told us to vote for ourselves so that we would register at least one vote in our favour. The expectations were not high. The mainstream parties had laid plenty of sieges against us and the media at large were predicting that the average Referendum Party candidate wouldn't score a vote higher than 1% of their constituency total. The regional campaign manager kept telling me if I scored anywhere near 2% I should be pleased. Anything over 3% was going to be exceptional. I was going to feel disappointed if I didn't score over 2.5%. I had campaigned hard, knocked on plenty of doors and had spoken well in debates, and a weak result would have made me question whether the regime could ever really be assailed by the power of the people. After all, if a billionaire squared up against the political classes and couldn't make a dent then who or what could? But Sir James always said that, even if we didn't win a single seat, at least we would have put the referendum issue firmly in the public consciousness, where it could only grow and perhaps one day lead to a big enough public stirring to make a difference. He told us to urge people to vote with their *conscience* and forget about who gets into power because Brussels ran the show anyway, not Westminster.

I scored 3.8% of the vote in my constituency, winning 2,196 votes and was among the highest scoring Referendum Party candidates anywhere in the country – although I was just crazy enough to think I might surprise everyone by pulling out a gorilla-sized upset to win the seat! But there was no disappointment whatsoever. The final election result showed that the Referendum Party had won a staggering 811,849 votes nationally, placing us fourth in the overall table of parties that had contested the election, of which there were just under fifty in total including the Green Party and the UK Independence Party, both which came nowhere near our numbers. Old

Willoughby had been right, British politics had never seen anything like it!

Sir James Goldsmith and the rest of us had certainly caused a stir but it wasn't to last. Shortly after the election Sir James died of cancer. This misfortune had the one positive consequence of dispelling all the press speculation that Goldsmith had an ulterior motive for forming the Referendum Party, which couldn't have been the case when he knew he would not live to see its fruition. No, this man had fought on principle. To his grave he took a conviction that had filled many with a belief that democracy *could* work but that it must not be taken for granted, indeed it needed to be protected and fought for.

I never tried to ingratiate myself into the power hierarchies that begun to take over the Referendum Party machine after he died. I felt I had added my light to Goldsmith's sum of light and had done as much as I could at that time. Instead I thought about how Tolstoy might have come home from faraway theatres of war, perhaps weary and cynical, but still committed to his ideals and eager for his writing mind to pick up where his fighting hands had left off. The sword now had to give way to the pen.

# THE PENDULUM SWINGS

As 1998 came around I tried developing a political novel called *Europia* - a story set in 2050 that took a cynical view about the failed utopia that a politically unified Europe was meant to be. I sent an outline to various agents and publishers but nobody liked it. Maybe they were all Europhiles and wanted to suppress opposition to their political sympathies but I wasn't about to get paranoid about it. Maybe I was just a bad novelist!

Eventually I put *Europia* in the drawer and started thinking I had to write something more commercial before turning my attention to loftier goals. I began writing a screenplay called *Gigolos* - which was a comedy-drama about a struggling, London actor who works as a male escort in-between acting jobs to help pay the bills. It was the kind of glossy, mainstream fare designed to be a cool summer blockbuster with a hip soundtrack, although at its heart it was quite a sincere love story where the main character learns that sex and love are two different things; this much I had learned from my own relationship.

Joanne and I were enjoying an idyllic, blissful time complete with nice holidays abroad and all sorts of dreams about our future. Love between us had been perfect so far. Joanne had been a strong force at my side during the election and had even acted as the official election agent during my campaign; a key role that involves managing the campaign budget and collating all sorts of paperwork that would otherwise bog down the candidate.

Our love was surviving the tests of everyday habits and personality traits but I couldn't help wondering how long this immaculate situation could go on for. Did love itself have a lifespan, some mysterious, organic process whereby its own peculiar nature determines when it lives and dies? The thought made me recall a conversation I had with a theatre friend in New York some years earlier on the topic.

"If you're ever in love and it falls apart look on the bright side," this friend told me, "you're a writer, an artist, nothing bad can happen to you because *it's all material.*"

It was interesting advice.

By the end of 1998 I had a draft of *Gigolos* ready to shop around and off it went in padded envelopes, only to get rejected by every major film production company in the country, very often getting returned without even being read! In the spring of 1999 I decided to call myself an independent producer and took the different approach of trying to attach enough star names to the project to raise the finance independently and, in the process, lift two fingers to a UK film industry that I had found ridden with cliques and not really an industry at all but more like a kind of establishment for members only.

I sent the script to Raquel Welch's agent in LA for the 1960's screen goddess to consider playing the Madam-cum-boss of the escort agency and to my surprise received a formal letter of interest from her agent confirming that she would agree to play the part subject to my raising the finance. Buoyed by this I took the same route and very quickly attached English names such as 1960's pop idol Adam Faith and 1970's movie stud Oliver Tobias to play aging, wise-cracking former escorts. And before the end of 1999 I also had Luke Goss from the 1980's British boy band *Bros* confirmed to play the lead.

Somehow I managed to juggle my day job and the demands of acting as a fledgling independent film producer but as 1999 wound down I started to lose enthusiasm for *Gigolos*. Despite the modest progress I wasn't getting anywhere with the finance and started to think I should instead just roll the dice wholeheartedly on something that really came from the heart. With scripts coming and going all the time Raquel and the others were perfectly understanding.

And so in the spring of 2000 I started to think about making a movie that blended the themes of love, spirituality and politics. But I also needed to come up with a story that could be produced on a budget I could personally afford since I didn't want to spend another year or longer trying to attach stars to cover a six-figure budget, nor did I want to go crawling back to the aloof London movie mob. The movie was going to be guerrilla stuff all the way. I wanted to cast unknown actors and direct the movie myself and was absolutely determined it would see the inside of a cinema. *Blair Witch*, Lars von Trier and the whole DV moviemaking revolution had come along at just the right time.

The making of a two-hour independent movie was going to require the mobilisation of a well-organised force so I wrote to my local newspaper *The Bucks Herald* and told them I was forming a new community arts group to be called the Aylesbury Film Company. The paper was quick to show interest and over coffee I told an intrepid young reporter that the AFC planned to draw on untapped talent within the community to make socially relevant movies using DV cameras on a shoestring budget.

I went on to reveal the basic story of *Jesus the Curry King* and spoke optimistically about my intentions to get the movie shown in cinemas, using *The Blair Witch Project* as my example and inspiration. In the interview I appealed for aspiring actors of any age to come forward and for anyone with a technical background to volunteer.

On April 8th 2000 *The Bucks Herald* ran a full page article on the story with the headline *The Town That Could Be Hollywood* which included my email address and telephone number for interested people to get in contact. To my surprise almost three hundred local people either emailed or left messages on my answering machine within days of the article appearing.

It was a galvanising response and I swelled with optimism. But this gargantuan public stirring did not guarantee that enough genuinely talented actors were at my disposal or that an elite squad of guerrilla movie makers were necessarily lying dormant. Somehow I had to dissect this fat belly of interest and extract the vital organs. I decided to call a meeting and found a local theatre willing to let me use one of their auditoriums.

On May 8th 2000 I took to the stage at Aylesbury's Limelight Theatre to tell a packed audience what the Aylesbury Film Company was going to be all about. I told them I wanted to bring the white and Asian communities of the town together in the making of the movie to achieve in practice what the fictional story aspired toward, to prove that different cultures *can* unite and work together. Here was a chance, I told them, to succeed in reality with what the character of Jesus sets out to do, and to make a real, tangible impact on cultural relations in our own town. Although, as I looked across the audience I could see just a single Asian face, which hardly suggested that cultures were going to be untied by the movie. Recruiting local Muslims and Hindus was clearly going to be the first practical challenge!

At the end of the meeting everyone interested in trying out for a part took turns saying their name and age to a DV camcorder that I had set up on a tripod in order to have a visual record of who was available to me. Names, addresses, telephone numbers and email addresses were also taken down on a clipboard along with what specific role each individual was happy to volunteer for. Nobody was getting paid but they all understood this wasn't really a commercial exercise. I finished by saying that the production would commence over the summer and that I would be back in touch with everyone more directly with regards to the casting and shooting schedule over the coming weeks. I hadn't even started on the script yet but assured everyone I could knock it out in good speed.

Since none of this was something I could manage on a part-time basis I quit my job and took out a sizeable personal loan, as well as applying for as many credit cards as I could, to help pay the rent and cover the budget for the movie. I didn't have any concern about going into debt to pay my way through the next six months because my confidence was sky high that the outcome would make the risk worth taking.

By then Joanne and I were living together in a rented, one bedroom apartment which she contributed toward from her student loan. She was three years into a business degree course at university and starting to develop her own outlook on life, which included an interest in animal welfare. She wanted to take time out to travel to the island of Borneo in South East Asia to help a charity dedicated to saving the Orang-utan population from extinction, and planned to spend six weeks in Borneo at a sanctuary in the jungle followed by a month travelling Bali and Australia as a tourist.

The timing was perfect because while she would be away I would be occupied with the hectic process of writing and directing my movie and wouldn't miss her as much as a result. It was wonderful to see this bright girl blossom into a young woman with such a great sense of compassion. I respected her. As I continued to learn about love I realised there can be no love without respect.

We had our spats, of course; arguments over silly things, important things and things we couldn't even remember when the arguing was over. That was the best thing about love, that it kept coming back after all was said and done, never wanting to give up no matter what the bad times. Even if love expires between two people the feeling itself is always ready to take us back in the guise of someone new, always without prejudice or fatigue, always without bitterness or apprehension, as fresh and powerful as whenever it first awoke in the world. What a marvellous thing. What hope there really is! What love story could I possibly come up with to do it justice?

I decided that, along with Jesus being resurrected in the modern day world, his original true love, Mary Magdalene, would return also. In Mary's case her spirit would enter the mind and body of a young girl working in public relations, enabling her to guide the miracle working chef through the pitfalls of becoming a media celebrity. In this way the aspect of love as a *partnership* could be symbolised. I also decided to resurrect Mary's spirit in an Asian girl to further underline how love transcends race, culture and religion. I had my love story – or as much of one as I could muster at that time in my life.

Next I needed an actor and actress who could be believable in the lead roles. Whilst a lot of the local acting talent from Aylesbury had been just right to fill most of the supporting parts it was crucial that the leads were as close to professional standard as possible. I found out there was a London newsletter called *PCR* which producers could advertise in free of charge. *PCR* stood for *Production Casting Report* and its subscribers were mostly up-and-coming actors, many of whom had professional training and minor credits to their name who didn't mind gaining experience on low budget, no-pay independent movies like mine.

Within a week of posting the casting call I had close to four hundred head shots land on my doormat which I quickly filed down to a handful. I then invited a short list of actors and actresses to Aylesbury where I again made use of the Limelight Theatre to audition them. For the several that couldn't make it to Aylesbury I arranged to meet them over two days in London in the comfortable lounge bar at the Grafton Hotel on Tottenham Court Road.

An exceptional, theatre-trained London actor of not obvious Italian descent called Marcello Marascalchi was eventually picked to play Jesus and a beautiful young Asian girl named Pooja Shah was a natural to play Mary. In Aylesbury I finally managed to rally enough local Asians, mostly non-actors, to give the movie the racial blend it needed thanks to an appeal by the Mayor of Aylesbury at the time, Raj Khan, who also helped me secure the use of a local Indian restaurant where we could film most of the movie.

By the end of June all the cast were in place and the trusty Internet helped me to find a good deal on DV equipment hire. The five-week shooting schedule was set to commence from the first week of August and I retreated into an intense, creative cocoon to finish off the script while Joanne took off on her travels.

*Jesus the Curry King* ran ninety four minutes in length and had a speaking cast of fifty seven with over four hundred extras. It took six weeks to shoot and two months to edit. It was guerrilla stuff but turned out to be a real movie and even had its own original music score which a brilliant, local musician spent two and half months composing. I shot the movie using a hired Sony PD 150 DVCAM, together with a professional camera/ lighting operator who agreed to work at a cut rate. A team of fantastic local volunteers helped out and the Aylesbury Film

Company came of age with its first effort. It came in just under the £10,000 budget, half of which was funded by an arts grant from Aylesbury's very supportive district council. Such pride was born from it all, such togetherness forged among total strangers. Again, strangers proved nothing more than friends and comrades waiting to be made.

In the movie Jesus describes that a battle for the soul and destiny of Mankind is raging between the forces of Good and Evil and that each of us has an epic, vital role to play in which side wins. The first thing everyone in the story wanted to know, of course, was where did God fit into things? From the Indian restaurant that becomes his sanctuary Jesus told reporters that the supreme power from which all things come into being defies any description or name, that God is not a man or a place but quite simply an energy source without beginning or end. He said this energy couldn't be named by mere mortals any more authoritatively than a child would decide on the name of its parents. His best word for this power was simply the Spirit, the eternal energy within all things, the source from which we are born and into which we return.

The Spirit itself was inherently good but first to come out of its cosmological explosion and birth of universes at the beginning of time was its total opposite; a powerful, negatively charged sub-energy that represented the anger and displeasure felt when the blissfully peaceful cosmic seal was shattered in the first place. This sub-energy assumed the name Evil and vowed to terrorise everything in time and space that subsequently came into creation, since everything created represented the loss of the wholeness and perfect splendour that eternity used to be.

The power of Evil set out to destroy Mankind by tempting each member of the species down the path of self-interest, in order to make impossible the human harmony that would otherwise keep Evil at bay. The power of Good fought back by inspiring in Man a deep sense of oneness with all things, first through nature and then through *art and ritual* when the first civilisations began to flourish out of the formerly nomadic tradition. Across the entire world, in completely separate and diverse cultures, the *same* mythical stories and tribal practices could be found as the omnipresent Spirit sought to express – in a universal, symbolic manner – the reality of our common consciousness. But then the most unfortunate human error occurred and Evil had its chance to thwart everything after all ...

The fictional war raging between the unseen, cosmological forces of Good and Evil in *Jesus the Curry King* was drawing on the age-old *power of metaphor* and – just like in all the world's religions and mythologies – nothing in the story was intended to be taken literally. When I was first discovering my sense of spirituality in New York all those years earlier I hadn't ignored the traditional faiths when exploring what others had written on the subject. My experience of the Spirit had been that its language could really only be understood through metaphorical references, and what struck me about religion was that the Spirit did indeed seem to communicate with Mankind in this manner – except the metaphors were being taken as *fact* and generations of people were being shut out of the transcendent meaning as a result!

This was the human error that allowed the power of Evil its chance to spread division, which the literal interpretations of the world's religions subsequently proceeded to do. The whole point of the movie was to encourage people to relearn the metaphorical language that can bring us a true understanding of the Spirit.

The miracle working curry dishes that transform local racists, for example, symbolised how a recipe for harmony can exist if only the right ingredients could be mixed together. The emergence of Evil out of the cosmic womb symbolised how each human life, once born from the perfect encapsulation of the mother's navel, naturally struggles with a duality of feelings about this rude, new awakening called life. The act of Jesus being resurrected in the body of an ordinary man symbolised how the eternal Spirit exists at the centre of everyone. And the coma from which this ordinary man awoke to realise the godly presence within him symbolised the depths of consciousness that must be penetrated by all in order for that insight to be known.

Whenever you think you're reading something remotely spiritual always look at what might be *symbolised*, not what is literally portrayed. There's a different language at work and it can tell you everything you need to know. I eventually came to understand that a relationship with the Spirit did indeed go further than inspiring a sense of oneness with creation, since this on its own cannot assist the individual with the critical life choices that each, unique person has to make. And that, once the Spirit's symbolic language is unwrapped from its literal packaging, its timeless insights proceed to reward the initiated with exactly the perspective needed not just to experience harmony, but also to guide the life onto its highest road of destiny – no matter how many barriers or ogres abound!

In religion I found it exhilarating and demoralising in equal measure to see so much spiritual guidance being so eloquently expressed yet roundly misinterpreted. In the awesome mythologies of Christianity, for example, enlightening rites of passage *applicable to each of us* such as the Resurrection, the Last Supper and the downfall in the Garden of Eden were works of metaphorical genius that rattled like gold coins wasted in the pouch of a bush kangaroo!

How the laughter of Evil must have shook a thousand moons. We almost had it won. If only we could relearn the language! An American mythology scholar from the 20th century named Joseph Campbell understood this better than anyone and his classic 1949 book *The Hero with a Thousand Faces* ought to be thoroughly studied before anyone goes near the Bible or any of the other holy epics.

A special screening at the Odeon cinema in Aylesbury was held on November 18th 2000 for the town to come out and see what we'd achieved together. I hired a little Sanyo LCD video projector and ran the movie through it off tape directly from the DV camera. This amazed the cinema manager and chief projectionist who never realised that the video projection of a digital tape could look so good on a cinema screen.

As the doors to Screen 1 opened the five hundred or so seats were taken up almost equally by white people and Asians, all mixing together happily. Just a few months earlier there had been a race riot in the town centre after an Asian taxi cab driver had been beaten senseless by white youths who had refused to pay the fare. You wouldn't have known that by taking a glimpse at the audience that night. The principle of togetherness enshrined in the story was being *seen* in reality – and maybe we could repeat this everywhere!

The local newspaper *The Bucks Herald* ran a review that raved "Spice is Right", declaring that the fledgling Aylesbury Film Company had an undeniable triumph on its hands. Obviously the intention wasn't to stop there and having found the local Odeon manager so supportive in agreeing to the special screening it was a natural progression to approach Odeon's head office about showing the movie nationwide as a proper, commercial release.

And so it was that I organised the BAFTA screening and then went to meet Tony Giddings in January 2001 at the Odeon HQ in London's Leicester Square ...

By that time I was completely at the end of my plastic means of support and fighting off debt collectors daily so I went back to work, taking a full time job through a temp agency at a local life insurance firm doing basic data entry, which kept the bills paid as well as being flexible enough that I could take days off at short notice as and when I needed.

Within the seven days I had to get back to Odeon I decided I would go ahead and confirm that, come November, I would indeed be supplying digital projectors and all necessary technical support to show my movie. It didn't matter that I had yet to put a firm plan in place for this. After all, I had the next ten months to work on it.

Something else I wanted to do around the movie's release was hold public meetings to debate the issues that the story couldn't really expound on at length, such as politics, which my re-born Messiah urged everyone to question.

But this was no guise for any anti-EU rhetoric on my part since, ironically, my experience with the Referendum Party eventually brought me to the realisation that the democracy we were fighting for was actually not worth protecting in the first place! It was just as flawed as the dictatorship we were criticising and in fact the whole damn system needed overhauling.

During the election campaign I came into contact with a lot of well educated people in many diverse fields and often the topic of conversation would spill over from Europe into the wider areas of globalisation, free trade and particularly the influence of the *business world* in politics. A commonly held opinion seemed to be that fending off the dragon in Brussels didn't actually guarantee that our democracy would be won back because democracy at home was just as much out of the public's control; that multinational corporations wielded too much power and, indeed, that a campaign on *two* fronts had to be fought.

Curious about the opinion that the corporate world controlled politics at large I did my own, private research into how political parties are funded and influenced, and found that those people were *right*. Previously I had been under the impression that democracy meant that the majority of people in a society pick their leaders who in turn serve their best interests. But the reality is that political parties – regardless of being in opposition to one another – first and foremost represent virtually the same set of business interests. The common people are always a secondary consideration.

There is nothing conspiratorial about this. There is no shadowy elite at work. They are all out in the open. Anyone can do research on that wonderful all-seeing eye the Internet to find out who the top ten donors are for any particular political organisation and it is not difficult to trace a line between those donors and the policies that their politicians pursue. Some rebel politicians struggle with this but not the ones who rise through the party ranks to achieve real power.

As it happens, society has not done too badly under this system. Even the lowest paid worker can soak in a bubbly hot tub, knock back a bottle of bargain priced Chardonnay and enjoy an experience of comparative luxury that would have been possible only for the kings and queens of the medieval era. With all the utilities available to the modern industrialised world a lot is owed to business enterprise.

But the problem has been that the business world and the politicians they accept as their public faces are far too content with the extremes of rich and poor that their profit culture has created. It's not a problem of capitalism but a mentality issue. This unfortunate mentality extends into how international businesses are all too easily inclined to instruct their politicians to wage wars to settle trade and investment disputes.

It is by now wearily accepted as a fact that no war was ever fought to save a population or advance humanity but rather to compete for the natural resources of a particular geographical region. The map of the world is drawn in *business boundaries*, the borders of what anyone thinks is their country is incidental as far as politicians and their business masters are concerned. Democracy of some kind did seem to exist, except the voice of Big Business was listened to above all others. Was this right? I didn't think so.

There was indeed something of a battle raging between the forces of Good and Evil for the destiny of Mankind and the dark arts were winning with their seduction of those who could all too easily be persuaded to abandon the common interest. Something had to be done.

Through public discussion I wanted to find out if anyone else shared these views, see what examples could be drawn and then see what ideas we could come up with to do something about it. I wasn't saying I had the answers but I was prepared to look for some. This made *Jesus the Curry King* not just a socially conscious movie but a social experiment and this is what I mean when I say I was serious about starting a revolution. This was no whim.

With Odeon supporting me, almost as if the heavyweight exhibitor was assisting the crusade without even knowing it, I set about putting my campaign into action by researching on the Internet to find out who I could approach about digital projectors. I quickly found that a number of major manufacturers were already clamouring around the cinema industry trying to jostle for position in what seemed like an emerging market.

It appeared that George Lucas, the man behind *Star Wars*, was largely responsible for the gold rush. Lucas had been a leading advocate of shooting movies in high definition digital video format and was very supportive about the digital projection of movies in cinemas versus the old film method. The 1999 release of the *Star Wars* prequel *Star Wars: Episode One: The Phantom Menace* had combined lot of high definition video production with celluloid film production and on June 18th of that year two movie theatres in the US were treated to special, all digital screenings of the movie on the best high definition digital projectors 1999 had to offer. Audiences loved the digital version and Lucas declared that film wouldn't play any part in the shooting of his next two *Star Wars* prequels and that digital projection would be preferred over film where possible.

This created an expectation that if Lucas said the digital format was superior to film then all of Hollywood would follow and the biggest technological transition in the movie business since the birth of sound and colour must be just around the corner. From my point of view it was especially fortuitous to see that digital projection in cinemas was not light years away otherwise I would have come onto the scene with my DV movie far too early. As it happened I had hit upon an impending transition at a very convenient time.

Big studio movies that followed *The Phantom Menace* onto digital screens in 1999 included Disney's *Tarzan* in July, *Toy Story 2* in November and *Bicentennial Man* in December. But that was it, just four digitally projected movies playing limited, digital engagements only. The following year would prove no watershed either with just twelve Hollywood movies getting a digital outing of some kind, beginning with *Mission to Mars* in March and ending with *Emperor's New Groove* in December. It was clearly very early days for digital cinema.

Whilst the innovations in digital projection was the main catalyst for the advent of digital cinema there were still a number of other, critical links involved in a digital movie release. These included the delivery of the content to the cinema and the means by which it would be stored and played out to the digital projector. With digital TV solutions already rejected by Hollywood I came across an all out war among competing,

international technology vendors to fill the gaps and win a blood
oath endorsement from Lucas and Hollywood.

Every major satellite and telecommunications provider on the
planet from British Telecom, France Telecom and Deutsche
Telecom in Europe to the likes of Boeing and Hughes Network
Systems in the US were fighting for supremacy in offering
bespoke distribution services as well as every small scale
operator from Singapore to Sao Paulo sprouting up with master
plans of their own.

The battle to electronically store and play out the digital files
was just as hotly contested by a similar array of global players in
the media server market from European giants such as EVS in
Belgium to California-based industry leaders Avica. And they
were by no means the only ones. It was a total feeding frenzy. I
felt like an early Wild West pilgrim who had ambled
unsuspectingly over a grass verge to suddenly behold the sight
of a massive, stampeding land rush!

But what particularly struck me was that, so far, nobody had
grouped all the separate, interdependent technology providers
together into a single, cohesive team in order to offer a complete
end-to-end distribution platform for releasing digital content
into cinemas. Instead, all those manufacturers were running
around the marketplace promoting their individual products
without any thought toward integrating their companies into
strategic alliances that would make them stronger together than
they were apart.

A light bulb suddenly went off in my head. If I could bring all
the necessary vendors together for *Jesus the Curry King*'s digital
release then why not turn my technology partnership into a
permanent team and fill that void? And rather than my DV movie
being an isolated project it could instead launch what would
effectively become the industry's first fully blown digital distribution business! The entrepreneurialism of it appealed to me and
none of it needed to compromise my larger social objectives. On
the contrary I saw how creating my own digital distribution
network could serve my agenda by permanently removing the film
distribution barrier for all the socially relevant movies I wanted to
make in the future under the Aylesbury Film Company banner.

Seizing this initiative seemed perfectly in alignment with my whole agenda so I decided to take a shot at it. Next I needed some kind of corporate name for my digital venture, an umbrella identity over and above the company brands that would comprise the interdependent links, and I came up with the name Quantum Digital, which I thought sounded "blue chip" and trustworthy.

I got back in touch with Odeon to beg a meeting with the Chief Executive, Richard Segal. If I was intending to use my movie's digital release to launch Quantum Digital I needed the whole project to be rephrased as being a trial of the technology which, if successful, had the option to roll out as a permanent digital network. This was something the man at the top would need to agree to and I was immensely encouraged when a date in late March 2001 was set to discuss the idea.

In the meantime I set about meeting all the major companies competing for ascendancy as digital cinema gathered pace, to see who might be keen to support my project. I explained my intentions and didn't pretend to be anything other than a low budget moviemaker who just wanted to show some entrepreneurial spirit. I needed everything for free, at least as far as *Jesus the Curry King* was concerned. Beyond this I speculated that sustainable business models to keep the kit installed on a permanent basis could include US film studios and other content providers paying a competitive price for a digital release versus film costs, as well as the possibility of Odeon or a sponsor contributing.

It turned out that a lot of these technology companies had R&D budgets that allowed experimental projects such as mine to be taken on from time to time, which was fortuitous given my humble financial situation. It also turned out that the idea of someone acting as a central co-ordinator for the myriad of technologies involved in digital distribution seemed viable and timely to just about everyone I contacted. Having the interest of Odeon also helped my proposition. The marketing value of conducting a digital experiment with the UK's largest exhibitor was not underestimated by anyone. To my amazement it proved a virtually effortless task to recruit all the technology partner-

ships I needed to guarantee the digital release of my movie and
the launch of Quantum Digital!

In less than three weeks I had industry leading brands such as
Barco pledging digital projectors, EVS pledging media servers,
France Telecom pledging satellite services and Dolby pledging
audio equipment. This could have given me pause for
celebration since only two months earlier just to get the
equipment on terms I could manage had been the critical
objective. But I was looking beyond that now and the cork
popping had to wait. Odeon still had to bite.

"We're very keen to remain at the forefront of using new
technology," Odeon CEO Richard Segal told me at our
meeting.

Odeon had been the first UK exhibitor to introduce bookings
via cellular phones, as well as over the Internet, and Richard
told me Odeon was also the first cinema chain in the country to
install a digital projector, which had been a prototype model at
Odeon Leicester Square co-funded by Disney and Texas
Instruments. The latter had developed something called DLP™
technology, which stood for Digital Light Processing™ – which
was the microchip of choice for digital projectors as far as
Hollywood was concerned. Texas Instruments had licensed their
DLP Cinema™ chip to a select number of manufacturers, Barco
among them, and were being chased in the market by the likes of
Sony, NEC and JVC, among others.

Segal was a firm believer that digital technology would
overhaul the cinema industry but that alternative programming
such as music, sport, theatre shows and interactive games would
prove to be the real boon when the transition occurred. Earlier
that month, on March 10th, this view had been supported by the
satellite transmission to ten US cinemas of a Broadway musical
called *Jekyll and Hyde,* which had been recorded live, in high
definition video and Dolby digital 5.1 surround-sound, and
shown on DLP™ projectors, courtesy of a partnership between
digital cinema entrant Boeing and a New York production
company called Broadway Television Network. The screenings
had been a wild success and did a lot to underline the potential
of alternative content.

But the number of digital movies shown on the DLP™ projector at Odeon Leicester Square and elsewhere was still few and far between. Because of this Segal didn't expect the wholesale digitisation of Hollywood movies was anywhere near to happening. Given this he wanted to know what my vision for Quantum Digital was. I said high profile alternative content could be the primary target and whichever Hollywood movies came along in digital format could be slotted in as well on some basis.

As 2001 was unfolding the list of major motion pictures that had already been digitally projected included *Vertical Limit, Pay It Forward* and *Miss Congeniality*, with major titles such as *Shrek, Jurassic Park III, Planet of the Apes* and *Monsters Inc.* also expected to receive digital outings before the year was out. If I could equip Odeon with the top of the range DLP™ kit there was every reason to believe the US studios would work with us to take advantage of a digital network in the UK, boosting Odeon's market leadership credentials as well as giving the chain a head start in experimenting with alternative content. There was no downside.

But I maintained that, on a more personal level, I had ideas for distributing socially relevant movies that were part of a bigger agenda, such as *Jesus the Curry King,* and that I would want to facilitate at least two or three digital movies per year that kept to these principles even if it wasn't the Aylesbury Film Company that produced them. There was always the possibility I might come across a brilliant new director, struggling to escape some ghetto wasteland, whose script efforts would ordinarily be tossed in the trash by the fenced-in London movie mafia.

If I could help new digital moviemakers like me reach audiences it would be great to establish what I started to call a "digital democracy", where the high finance brigade would no longer monopolise the means of production and distribution as they had done throughout the century of celluloid. Segal warmed to this, saying Odeon had always been a champion of independent movies and that he could see the potential of digital cinema to help more new directors on the fringe to break through.

I told Segal the revenue stream to pay for the equipment going forwards could be looked at once we had proved to the industry that our network actually worked. For now the Quantum Digital consortium just wanted to concentrate on *Jesus the Curry King* as the test case, promote it to the hilt and then see where it took us. I told Segal I wasn't, so far, talking to any other cinema chain and that Quantum would be quite prepared to work exclusively with Odeon. So, was he in or out?

Richard Segal said yes to everything! The man brimmed with an enthusiasm and visionary zest that couldn't have been more ideal if I'd scripted it! I was elated and could hardly believe the pace of developments. Two months earlier I had been technically illiterate with my movie hovering in limbo land and now its distribution was guaranteed. And there I was discussing digital cinema with all the big names in the business as a virtual expert on the subject! If all went to plan *Jesus the Curry King* would also win the historic distinction of becoming the first feature film in UK to be produced, distributed and exhibited exclusively in the digital format in cinemas across the country. This was a milestone I started to covet as much as anything.

Within a week I received an official letter from Richard Segal confirming that the digital screening of my movie would serve as a trial for Quantum Digital to launch a digital network at Odeon, with the first week of November 2001 set as the movie's release date. The locations spanned the geographical range of the UK, including Glasgow, Brighton, Liverpool, Birmingham and my home town of Aylesbury of course. Overall the movie was booked to play on eight screens across the country, which was perfect from the point of view of taking my activist campaign right around the nation. My consortium had almost eight months for the logistics to be worked out and in the meantime I could refocus some much needed attention on the movie itself. There was the promotion of it to get busy with, along with figuring out exactly how and where I was going to stage the public meetings.

I set about hounding a reporter from *The Daily Telegraph* called Chris Hastings, who had come across *Jesus the Curry*

*King* when the trade magazine *Screen International* had given it a brief mention in 2000. Chris told me to keep him informed about its progress since new, independent movies were always interesting to cover. Now that I had my big Odeon news to report, along with the digital aspect, Chris was happy to write an article on it with the headline "£10,000 Film To Get Nationwide Release" which appeared in *The Sunday Telegraph* on March 18th.

The very next morning I received a telephone call from a news producer at the BBC1 breakfast show programme saying she had read the newspaper article and was interested to have me and the actor who played Jesus on their programme for a live interview. Getting on the BBC, the UK's best known television broadcaster, wasn't even something I was going to attempt but there they were coming to me! I certainly wasn't going to decline the opportunity and neither was Marcello Marascalchi, who played the Curry King and on Friday March 23rd at 8:20 am we graced the breakfast sofas at the BBC studio in London to talk about the movie. They even ran a thirty-second clip, which thrilled the hell out of us.

Two days later I got a call from another breakfast show producer, this time from Channel Four's morning show, *The Big Breakfast*, asking if Jesus and me wanted to come on their show too for another live interview? The following week we were back on national television spreading the word about *Jesus the Curry King*'s November release and this time I talked a bit more about the fact that it would mark a technological milestone by becoming the first movie ever to play in UK cinemas without film playing a part at any stage. My digital ambitions for Quantum Digital to blaze a trail in the industry were increasingly pushing to the forefront of my mind and I wanted to capitalise on the publicity to raise awareness about the concept of digital cinema.

Both TV interviews went extremely well and Marcello must have thought the big break all actors dream about was suddenly happening for him. It felt like I was finally going to experience a major breakthrough with my own dreams too after so many years of trying with various projects. By April I had a nice little press kit assembled which included VHS tapes of our TV interviews along with newspaper cuttings from *The Sunday Telegraph* and *The Bucks Herald* and I planned to spend the summer of 2001 publicising the movie as widely as possible through every radio, TV and print media outlet in the country. The revolution I dreamed of making a reality was getting closer and closer and it wasn't turning out to be some radical long shot either. I was actually getting somewhere!

I planned to hold the public meetings in local town halls or community centres and the running order would involve two forty-five minute sessions, separated by an interval and followed by a Q&A at the end.

In the first half I could discuss the deficiencies of modern democracy and invite debate on possible solutions. And in the second half I could interpret the metaphorical language of the world's great faiths to show how the Spirit has operated through all of them in exactly the same way – with a striking, undeniable consistency running through the mystical folklore and ritual traditions of every culture the world has ever known.

From Algonquin natives to Aztec warriors, from ancient Greek poets to early Semitic historians, from the mythic imagination of Neolithic cave painters to the classical divinity of Michelangelo's chapel art, *one voice* could truly be heard rolling off the localised dialect of many tongues. Throughout the ages exactly the same thing gets said about our fundamental unity and journey through life, with the style and emphasis of the timeless instruction altering only to match the specific environment and evolutionary stage of each, particular culture.

Nothing new needs to be said since it has all been said before. The trick has always been to find ways to keep the language fresh and functional in a changing world, to upgrade the software you might say – and then, if possible, to keep it virus-free!

Where the symbolical referencing was once the work of the tribal shaman and religious elders today it is the work of the creative artist – the writer, actor, musician, dancer, painter and poet – because *the import of the sublime* in the modern world is achieved nowhere better than in popular art. Sometimes knowingly and sometimes intuitively the great artists do not fail us. And likewise, sometimes knowingly and sometimes intuitively, we connect to the transcendent power. From James Joyce to Pablo Picasso to George Lucas, among many others across all the artistic mediums, the eternal language has found bountiful resonance in those artists with a very special light that is always on.

At the end of the meetings I planned to have volunteers on hand with clipboards for people to supply their contact details if they decided they wanted to officially join the movement. I had no idea what I'd do after that. I was relying on the input of others. The important thing was to make a start and just have faith.

I planned to work through local newspapers to promote the public meetings at the same time as publicising the movie release and would also try to get local reporters along to the meetings to help generate further awareness about what I was trying to do. If I could sign up ten thousand people by the end of the year and succeed in bringing a mix of cultures together in the process I thought it would be a good start.

It was clear that before long I would have to quit my day job in order to devote my full and proper attention to all this and I had to hope the movie and launch of Quantum Digital would make at least enough money to sustain me. I didn't care about making huge profits from any of it, although I wasn't against material desire or personal wealth either. As far as I was concerned we didn't need to tear down the capitalist system to fix things, we just needed to make a few adjustments. After all, the capitalist system hadn't stopped me finding my spirituality and it didn't need to stop anyone else finding theirs either.

But it did start to cross my mind that launching Quantum Digital had the potential to raise my financial status enormously. If it did I simply told myself that as long as I continued to put my spiritualism above materialism I would be okay. It was a question of *balance*. Men like software mogul Bill Gates and media baron Ted Turner had made headlines by donating massive sums to charity, proving that money didn't have to be the enemy of a better world. It seemed money was a totally neutral force which could only be characterised as good or evil depending on what was done or not done with it. I found it such a terrible misconception for money to be considered the root of all evil. The roots were deeper than that.

Somewhere in all of this I was still trying to understand love! For the first time Joanne and I had started to encounter serious problems. Ironically money was an issue. With all my trips to London and days off work I was struggling to cover the bills and, although Joanne was contributing more or less evenly, things were tight and it put a tremendous strain on our relationship. Love, it seemed, had a cost! There was no cynicism about this. It is perfectly reasonable to rationalise that without money any relationship in the world is going to struggle. I don't expect we were the only couple to be tested by the issue of money, or the lack of it, and if our attitudes on the subject had not been so divergent I doubt the cracks would have begun to appear.

My gut feeling was that all we had to do was get to November and that my movie would start to repay my faith in the entire project, but Joanne was reacting badly to what she saw as an unacceptably cavalier attitude towards our finances. I was dismissive of this only because I believed in my future, and deep down I knew she did too, but this didn't stop the arguments. I could have tried harder to listen and reassure her but it wasn't the best time for emotional headaches. I needed all my wits about me going into the summer and my relationship became steadily marginalised as my movie and the launch of Quantum Digital assumed top priority.

In the late spring I had suggested to my consortium and to Richard Segal that we should stage a presentation day a month prior to the movie release and invite the industry and media to come and see what we were trialling, that this might succeed in attracting the interest of US film studios, potential sponsors and just make for good old fashioned PR, not least for my movie. Everyone agreed it was a good idea to demonstrate how the network functioned, which could include product demonstrations, a Q&A session and a cosy tea and coffee reception afterwards for business cards to be exchanged.

Segal volunteered the use of Screen One at Odeon West End in Leicester Square and my consortium readily pledged all the kit. Our special event was set for October 4th and hundreds upon hundreds of invites went out with a good rate of RSVP replies. My technical team were increasingly keen to make their credentials known to film circles and urged me to approach the major US studios to see if we could digitise some Hollywood film material and show it during our presentation.

With all the big brands I had under the Quantum umbrella I didn't have much trouble securing approvals from the likes of Disney and Warner Brothers to show the digital versions of some of their upcoming movie trailers, and our special event was on course to demonstrate the most ambitious and forward thinking digital cinema undertaking so far seen anywhere in the industry. I doubt anyone could have imagined I was flat broke, living on a diet of bargain priced pasta, monstrously in debt and on the verge of personal oblivion. I just kept telling myself to stay afloat until November when the box office returns of my movie would rescue me and the public meetings would put fresh adrenaline in my veins.

Then something unexpected occurred. A man called Phil Barlow from Disney, who was the US studio's digital cinema figurehead at the time, suddenly developed the opinion that *Jesus the Curry King* shouldn't be the material used in the trial. He argued that showing a movie shot on DV in a major digital cinema trial was not representing the highest quality that digital cinema had to offer and that audiences might get turned off the concept altogether if the November event proceeded with such a low budget affair.

I was stunned, horrified and politely defiant. I explained to Barlow, who had been my contact at Disney for the movie trailers they were supplying, that *Jesus the Curry King* represented more than just a trial of digital technology; that it had a message, was part of a bigger agenda and that I was already well along the path of publicising the movie in the national press. The launch of Quantum Digital would lose all meaning if I replaced *Jesus the Curry King* with a digitised 35mm feature film or a high definition video programme of some kind. Scrapping all my preparation now would amount to the collapse of my entire revolution and my whole life's sense of purpose would be swept aside in one ugly stroke! It was simply out of the question.

But Barlow was insistent and even lost his temper and started screaming down the telephone at me from his office in Los Angeles, saying that The Walt Disney Company shouldn't be underestimated by anyone who wanted to get ahead in digital cinema and that the industry would be a much friendlier place for me to be if I respected the right people. I couldn't believe what I was hearing. In slightly quivering tones I tried to continue my counter-argument, saying that the beauty of digital cinema was precisely that it *did* enable new moviemakers shooting on cost efficient formats the ability to reach the public, and that surely audiences would realise that my low budget guerrilla effort was an example of this and not the upper scale of what the format could offer.

But the man was totally inflexible and seemed offended that I had even dared to debate the matter. He finished the brief, acidic conversation by telling me to go away and think about it. If I went ahead with *Jesus the Curry King* he would renege on supplying material for the presentation day and the name Quantum Digital would be mud in Hollywood.

I wanted to laugh it off the way you do at a jumpy moment in a horror movie but this monster didn't look like going away. His argument was irrational and I suspected there might be an ulterior motive at work, that perhaps Hollywood didn't want to see a trend of low budget digital movies and alternative programming emerging at the onset of digital cinema as this would clearly threaten the monopoly that the major film distributors were used to enjoying when it came to booking content into cinemas. Whatever the case, I had a dilemma on my hands.

I conferred with my consortium and was not surprised to find them all nervous about the prospect of upsetting a big Hollywood studio. Barlow's belligerence was threatening to spread cracks through my entire alliance. But Odeon stood right behind me. Richard Segal said if I wanted to go ahead and show

*Jesus the Curry King* as planned he was happy for me to do it. I knew I could use this unequivocal support as leverage to muscle my team into delivering what they had promised and that they could probably get away with it without too much negative fallout. The question was whether I wanted a future for Quantum Digital as a serious player in the digital cinema marketplace because going against Disney was likely to be career suicide.

My instincts told me to defy him and trust the fates. The decision should have been easy. But something had already started to happen to me and looking back as I do now it is almost as though I am an outsider looking in on a man who had started to change in ways he wasn't even aware of. The change happened before he could lay the blame at Phil Barlow's door. Already a pendulum inside him had started to swing away from the exclusive pursuit of an ideal to something else, a commercial interest that was far more seductive than it first seemed ...

# - 4 -

# ONE REVOLUTION AT A TIME

Marc was beginning to wonder if the call would ever come. If it didn't come soon it was going to be too late to make the event happen at all, and the flower he saw his career as being was in danger of wilting.

"It's on!" Robert Young finally declared emphatically down the line from New York, where he was based.

"What date?"

"September 8th."

It was tight, by then it was already approaching mid-July.

"Barely eight weeks," Marc said ponderously.

"That's the minimum lead time you said."

That's what Marc had said but secretly he would have preferred a few weeks longer, although it wasn't a perfect science and there were no college courses or manuals for how to do any of this, except for the one he was making up as they went along.

"We'll make it!" Marc punched back.

It seemed that just enough alchemy had been stirred during the conference call with David Bowie's publicists a few weeks earlier for the brew to thicken. Over a year's work had gone into lobbying record labels and here was the chance for it all to pay off. It had the potential to make history and set a new trend in artist promotion, a trend that the ambitious young Englishman was perfectly poised to capitalise on.

"How many locations?" Marc quizzed.

"We're getting the final list from all the Sony affiliates in two or three days," Robert answered.

The Sony Music marketing family across the world had already been tipped off about this one and the list was expected to be long. The spirited Irishman was excited because he was going to get an executive producer credit on the show and a princely fee and probably rightly so. It had been Robert Young who had lined up Marc John's first big meeting with Sony Music in London, the meeting that saw him turn out in his finest Valentino lamb's wool suit complete with overpriced, hand woven Italian silk tie.

Marc had come striding along Great Marlborough that day as though his suit completed him, empowering him with a stature and confidence he once didn't need a masquerade of fabric to bestow. Indeed, when he paused outside the front entrance of the Sony Music UK offices at the sight of music biz types coming and going who resembled painters and decorators, it almost served to remind him of the deception of appearances. He whipped off his tie and ruffled his neatly parted, dark brown hair not because he had suddenly reconnected to this knowledge, but because he wanted to fit better into this new environment.

When the elevator doors parted on the fourth floor he had to snap himself out of thinking about the past, which he was prone to doing. It seemed old memories wanted to remind him about something, about the man he used to be. But now he had to get into that zone of his; a place of mental rigidity that he was convinced was a better methodology for functioning rather than finding a simple calm as he once would have done.

And as the jittery thirty-one year paced nervously around the Internet café along Tottenham Court Road many months later, waiting for one of Bowie's publicists to join the all important conference call, he was trying to muffle the deep breathing that was meant to relax him. But rather than operate from an even tempo he was now struggling with the rhythm of life's most natural law. He didn't get the hint in the moment that this was far more significant than it seemed on the surface. But it was on the surface of his being that he was living these days, not from its depths.

The opportunity to launch Quantum Digital and leap to the forefront of the industry had proved irresistible. He had given in to Disney bruiser Phil Barlow and cancelled the digital screenings of *Jesus the Curry King* along with the social experiment the project was meant to be. But in his mind he hadn't cancelled anything and was simply rescheduling. It was a strategic move, he told himself, to appease Hollywood, keep Disney onboard and then return to the social crusade a little later down the line.

"What's your fee going to be? We need to lock that down from the start," Robert told him during their telephone call.

"Depends on the final number of locations I suppose," Marc answered, "that will determine how much work is involved."

Sony Music were preparing to do the event around the world and under his Odeon contract Marc was permitted to offer consultancy services to other companies in cases where there was no conflict of interest. Given that Odeon only had cinemas in the UK there were no conflicts in Sony Music hiring Quantum Digital to organise the event outside the UK as well, to co-ordinate the cinema screenings of the show everywhere it played.

If everything went according to plan it would not only help attract future live events but virtually guarantee the renewal of his contract with Odeon, his principle paymaster. The Odeon deal was the financial glue that held his life together and keeping them happy was always the first consideration. So far Marc had yet to deliver any box office bonanzas but Odeon had been prepared to write off previous, low key screenings of alternative content as experimental. But mid-way through 2003, with six months remaining on his two year contract, he knew if he didn't deliver with the Bowie gig he could be back to a life of bargain priced pasta and cheap bottles of Merlot.

The Odeon contract was, ironically, an unexpected consequence of the Phil Barlow incident. Once Marc agreed to drop *Jesus the Curry King* something else had to be found to replace it in the technology trial. Initially Marc thought Barlow would approve the digital screening of something like *Monsters Inc.* which was due out in the UK around the same time. But when he reported back to the Disney heavyweight that all plans to show his DV movie had been scrapped the man from Los Angeles pulled an even bigger surprise by declining to have anything to do with Quantum Digital even though the plans had changed!

"We're just going to sit back and wait and see what you do," Phil Barlow told him.

Barlow also withdrew permission for Disney trailers to be shown during Quantum Digital's presentation day but told Marc it didn't mean that Quantum couldn't have a relationship with the studio in the future. Marc reeled, shocked and helpless. Reverting to the previous plan would still risk alienating the influential US studio yet now there was nothing to go forward with. The presentation day was fortunately not in jeopardy since Warner Bros were not reneging on their consent for the digitised trailers of *Harry Potter and the Philosopher's Stone* and *Miss Congeniality* to be shown. But the race was then on to find a substitute for *Jesus the Curry King* to announce at the presentation day as the UK's first nationwide all-digital theatrical release.

It was Mike Coleman, the UK business development manager for Barco, who suggested to Marc that he try contacting Broadway Television Network – the New York production company who had successfully screened a live recording of the Broadway musical *Jekyll & Hyde* in numerous US cinemas in March 2001 – to find out if a deal could be struck for Quantum to distribute the show in the UK as the replacement programme. The high definition production credentials and Dolby digital 5.1 sound format of *Jekyll & Hyde* made it a stellar example of what digital cinema had to offer, and Mike was certain that none of the Hollywood studios could reasonably object if the issue of technical standards was really their concern.

If a deal could be struck the trial would be saved, the presentation day would have its big news to announce and Quantum Digital would live to fight another day – and the revolution wouldn't necessarily be thwarted. Marc got on the telephone to New York and made the pitch and to his delight BTN President Bruce Brandwen was adventurous enough to show interest, even suggesting that his newest live recording of a Broadway musical, Stephen Sondheim's *Putting it Together*, might be a better title to take since it starred Ruthie Henshall, one of the darlings of London's West End theatre scene. A deal was in sight!

Marc got back to Odeon boss Richard Segal on the change of plan and there was even more good news. Odeon Leicester Square, Europe's largest cinema famed for glitzy movie premieres and located in the heart of London's West End, had a rare opening during November when *Putting it Together* could be shown in its main 2000-seat auditorium.

"We've got *Harry Potter and the Philosopher's Stone* opening on Friday the 16th but there's actually a small window between Monday the 12th and Thursday the 15th when we won't have anything running because we'll be getting the cinema ready, so you've got four days to play with," the ever buoyant Segal told him.

Not only was the venue perfect but the timing almost divine. Odeon Leicester Square was hardly ever available for short notice bookings and just as rarely available even if booking inquiries were made six or more months in advance. It was London's number one cinema and to hit on not one but four days during which a broke, hustling entrepreneur could have the Square all to himself was the stuff of improbable fantasy!

Things got even better. Odeon Leicester Square had all the digital kit already installed, of course, so from a technical standpoint none of the resources pledged by the Quantum Digital consortium were going to be needed. This meant Marc could bow to Disney and know he still had a wealth of complimentary equipment to call on at a later date to resume the social experiment of *Jesus the Curry King*. The only trade off was that *Putting it Together* would not run nationally, but it would still make history – marking the first time in history that a Broadway show had ever been seen in a cinema.

The Quantum man was playing Phil Barlow's game and felt he had retained the upper hand. A snarling gratification appeared on Marc's face when the deal memo he drafted for BTN and Odeon was signed. For the first time since he was a teenager Marc had felt a seething resentment for someone, an animosity that his wily dexterity had done little to alleviate. Barlow had attempted to rub out his precious business vision and the Englishman's cultivated mild manner had been chipped away at. Not that he realised any of this of course. Instead he felt justified and righteous.

On November the 13th and 14th 2001 two matinees and two evening performances of *Putting it Together* played to ecstatic crowds at Odeon Leicester Square, who even applauded in between the musical numbers! The show went out under the Quantum Digital banner and its success meant that Marc John's business vision found oxygen. Odeon were keen to repeat the innovation and claim market leadership in digital cinema and Marc was more than happy to seize a career niche that nobody else in the industry had identified. In fact the idea of creating a business development position within Odeon to advance digital programming was Marc's idea and Richard Segal had been entrepreneurial enough to run with it.

He now had an executive title, financial security and all that free equipment still available to him for a nationwide trial. As 2002 unfolded for Odeon's newly minted Head of Digital Cinema Marc John was perfectly poised to get the revolution back on track with more ammunition at his disposal than ever before. But he just wanted to get a few more things on the ball, get a few more big shows in the bag and make his position just a little bit stronger ...

He had got the big call from Robert Young at home, in the flat he occupied alone as a single man. He and Joanne were no longer together as a couple but this didn't trouble him. He knew she was happy again and the knowledge comforted him. Not that he had stopped thinking about her straight away. After she was first gone he thought about her every single day. He might have tried getting back with her if so many things hadn't started happening so quickly. He just couldn't fit in the time to care.

When the list came back from Sony it exceeded Robert's forecast, reaching close to ninety major cities in twenty two countries spanning five continents. Marc would have taken it on no matter what the scale. Robert Young had kept him updated over the summer regarding the number of Sony Music affiliate offices around the world who said they'd want to participate, so the scope had steadily become clear. One by one the Sony Music marketing directors around the world became acquainted with Marc as emails to and from the Sony Music headquarters in New York were copied to him. In this way Marc was adopted into the Sony Music family as the digital guru who was going to take care of everything for everyone, and knowing the likely locations gave him a head start in speculatively contacting cinemas and equipment personnel in anticipation of the green light.

His first task was to find out which cinemas existed in the chosen cities and then to make contact with the cinema managers to broker a deal to book the event. He encouraged the local Sony marketers to suggest cinemas they already knew, to save time, and plenty of preferences began trickling in. Elsewhere Marc picked the cinemas, drawing on his knowledge of the exhibition market which by then he could boast as exhaustive.

Not all the cinemas were going to need special equipment and the next task was to involve as many exhibitors as possible who were already incorporating digital projection into their businesses. This would keep the costs down for the local Sony Music offices, which would otherwise need to cover equipment hire charges out of their marketing budgets. Wherever the digital equipment didn't exist Marc would also draw on his resources to find a local supplier and arrange for temporary installations and technical supervision on the night of the show. With barely eight weeks to go and with nearly ninety cities to cover his right ear was going to grow a telephone!

His Odeon contract included the exclusive use of a private office with a big desk, telephone line and an Internet connection at the massive Odeon multiplex in Marc's home town of Aylesbury. This was especially convenient since it was just five minutes walk from where he lived and meant he could make all his business calls from the office rather than from home. Not that Marc wanted to put his feet up and puff on a pack of Havana cigars; he wanted to prove himself and repay Odeon's faith in him, feeling a genuine loyalty toward Odeon chief Richard Segal, who had really taken a chance on him.

One of the bargaining chips he was able to use to help secure his Odeon contract was the complimentary kit that his consortium had pledged for temporary use in a nationwide trial. He agreed to supply the kit, together with a broad range of alternative programming, within the first six months of his contract. And in April 2002 what was billed as the Odeon Digital Festival ran for two weeks across four locations including London, Brighton, Glasgow and Aylesbury of course.

The first week was called the BroadwayCinema™ festival since it featured three Broadway musicals supplied by Broadway Television Network in New York, with whom Marc was by then well acquainted from having brokered the Odeon Leicester Square screenings of *Putting it Together.* Marc followed up the relationship by proposing that *Jekyll & Hyde* and BTN's other hi-def musical, *Smokey Joe's Café,* get digital outings in the UK as well. A deal was made and the festival kicked off in high style.

The second week was a mixed bag of programmes including the opera *Rigoletto,* the ballet *Cinderella,* a taped performance of a 2001 live Robbie Williams concert in Cologne, a specially compiled edition of the classic children's show *Rainbow,* a sing-a-long version of Andrew Lloyd Webber's *Joseph and the Amazing Technicolor Dreamcoat* and a digitally restored version of David Lean's *Brief Encounter* – which Marc felt should be included even though it was a movie and not a piece of alternative programming. He saw Lean's black and white classic as a peerless benchmark of craft that new directors liberated by the digital age would do well to study rather than think they could call themselves directors just because it was finally economically feasible to do so.

Lastly and without much fanfare *Jesus the Curry King* took a slot in the festival. Marc couldn't let the use of the freebie kit come and go without his movie making it onto the screen, despite the fact that he had neither the time nor the focus to execute the larger social experiment as originally intended. But there was still the milestone of *Jesus the Curry King* being the first digital movie in the UK to be theatrically released in multiple theatres exclusively in the digital format and it also carried the torch for independent DV movies.

Amazingly he felt little regret over the virtual burial of his crusading movie in the festival. He still believed in the mighty showdown between Good and Evil, and that he had not laid down his sword but had simply yet to swing it. Besides, he couldn't do much without having a day job and at least his new vocation put him inside the business he always wanted to crack. He was only thirty and running a major, new department for one of the world's most prestigious names in cinema. His pioneering Hollywood hero Irving Thalberg might have been impressed. Indeed, Marc John was The Man! Whenever anything was happening with alternative content most people in digital cinema circles automatically assumed it was a Marc John project. Nobody had made such a specialty of alternative content until he'd come along and he revelled in being peerless. But privately he remained convinced that his status was being exalted only for the cause of good, that he had been placed on an unstoppable new track that was only going to make the revolution more formidable when it came.

The majority of the consortium weren't needed for the festival since everything ran from Panasonic HDD5 player decks and HD tapes directly into the Barco projectors, rather than being downloaded via satellite onto servers. This removed France Telecom and Belgium server specialist EVS from the equation respectively, although the consortium's glue had held together long enough for the presentation day to run as planned and all the participants benefited from the marketing profile as Marc had promised. But once Quantum Digital was taken under Odeon's wing the remit was to evaluate a host of technologies rather than jump into bed with single providers and, for the festival, only Barco and Dolby had remained as technical partners from the original consortium.

The festival attendance was poor and did nothing to show the potential of alternative programming. Even the Robbie Williams concert, which looked and sounded fantastic on the big screen, failed to attract significant numbers for the festival to be hailed a success. Marc blamed poor marketing, or rather zero marketing, on the part of Odeon's in-house and indifferent marketing department, although in fairness none of the content providers had been especially forthcoming with publicity efforts either. The whole affair was written off as a toe-in-the-water exercise with the lesson being that better marketing was the key factor going forwards.

The most favourable consequence of the festival was that a good relationship had been struck between Marc and IE Management, the people who handled Robbie Williams. IE were very interested in digital cinema as something that might suit a live Robbie concert sometime in the future and Gabby Chelmicka, one of Robbie's managers, promised to be in touch with Marc to follow up on the idea when the star was next on tour.

"Fifty thousand dollars," Marc told Robert from behind the big desk in his office, referring to his fee.

"You'll never get that, that's ten percent of the entire budget!"

"It's a fair price for the work involved," Marc countered bullishly.

"You've got to think long term," Robert pressed, "don't make this type of thing look too expensive otherwise we jeopardize getting events regularly. We've got to build this slowly, not look for jackpots straight away."

Marc wasn't looking for jackpots, just fair remuneration. Besides, he had already discounted his fee on a previous, smaller event that Quantum had organised for Sony Music which had served as the test case for them buying into it for Bowie. This event had featured the Grammy award winning American rock singer Melissa Etheridge, who had released a music DVD that spring called *Live and Alone*. Melissa was especially big in Germany and Holland and Sony Music had agreed to run with the idea of a cinema event to promote the DVD in those territories as well as to familiarise themselves with the concept in general.

The Melissa Etheridge event was shown in four German cinemas and a radio station studio in Hilversum, Holland, on May 16th 2003, and had been promoted with cinema trailers running four weeks in advance. It involved a live introduction by Melissa via satellite from Los Angeles followed by the DVD and concluded with a live question and session between Melissa in LA and pre-selected members of audiences across all the venues. Everything worked perfectly and the end result was gold. The fans loved it, Melissa Etheridge had a ball doing it and Sony Music was given the confidence to think bigger.

"This isn't Melissa, Robert," Marc argued congenially, "and didn't I already take a low fee on that one to show good faith?"

"You won't get fifty grand, that's all I'm saying."

Marc decided he would put the figure to Julie Borchard anyway, the senior Vice President of International Marketing at Sony Music who was overseeing the project and responsible for the budget. Besides having a professional relationship Julie and Robert were also a couple, Marc learned along the way, so the Irishman probably knew better than anyone what fee the Quantum man was likely to end up with. Julie was a tough cookie and Marc knew that haggling with her would be hard work in itself.

But he had a lot of respect for Julie, a woman who saw the digital future and bravely invited it into the present. It had been Julie who pushed the buttons to make the Melissa Etheridge event happen and she was now backing a far more ambitious, expensive and altogether riskier project. With an artist as important to everyone as David Bowie only an unqualified success was going to be acceptable. Careers can be made or broken on such things. This girl had guts! But, respect aside, business is business and The Man had to get a fair shake.

"But don't Odeon already cover you for anything you do in the UK?" Julie asked down the telephone, ready to haggle. "Shouldn't your fee reflect this?"

"It does, otherwise it'd be higher," Marc countered, just smoothly enough that it sounded honest, which it was.

Julie tossed lower numbers around and it was clear Marc wasn't going to get fifty thousand dollars. Finally they settled on something closer to thirty. For just under two months work, with the likely consequence of further live events and the extension of his Odeon contract, this was a figure Marc could live with.

Not that he expected the gig to be easy. He calculated that each venue was going to involve the participation of the cinema manger, probably the assistant manager, the cinema's chief projectionist, probably the duty projectionist, an engineer taking care of the satellite equipment, a technician taking care of the digital projector and, in some cases, an audio technician to operate the microphones and mixer boards for the live question and answer session planned at select locations.

All in all it came to a tally of roughly seven individuals per venue who needed to be brought onboard and managed. With approximately ninety venues to cater for this totalled over six hundred personnel that Marc would have to round up and supervise across a multitude of country borders and time zones. And it would be just him doing it. With the exception of just a few trusted stalwarts with whom Marc had forged ties during the making of *Jesus the Curry King* he rarely used anyone to work on behalf of Quantum Digital. He just didn't trust anyone enough with the responsibility. So far nothing had gone wrong with any of the events he'd organised, not the slightest glitch or embarrassing turn, and he couldn't afford for his impeccable reputation to take any knocks, especially now.

The project was basically going to involve a simultaneous approach to two, distinctly different sets of objectives. On the ground in London there would be the studio, the production, the satellite distribution and the digital 5.1 sound components to pull together and, around the world, the movie theatres would need to be found, equipped where necessary, tested and supervised. The overall budget for the event was somewhere around half a million dollars, with most of it allocated to the production. Part of Marc John's remit as the project co-ordinator was also to locate a suitable TV studio and even suggest production companies, all of which his Quantum Digital set-up purported it could do.

The marketing and promotion would be the job of Julie Borchard and the network of Sony Music offices around the world, although part of Marc's brokerage services between record labels and cinemas was also to make sure the cinema's local advertising mechanisms were fully utilised, such as local newspaper listings, local radio and cinema websites where possible. The commercial disappointment of the Odeon Digital Festival the year before was a lesson in the importance of marketing that wasn't going to be learned twice.

"Are you sure you can handle all of this?" Robert had asked.

"Don't worry about me," Marc assured him, "I eat, sleep and dream about this stuff!"

And he did. Except often they were nightmares, not dreams, nightmares of failure and horrendous embarrassment. Sometimes getting any kind of sleep at all was a problem. The worst of these nightmares usually involved him being summoned to Richard Segal's office to be told his contract was being cancelled. Another recurring nightmare was to wake up terrified halfway through the night, mistakenly thinking an event was supposed to have taken place earlier that evening but that he had overlooked something crucial, resulting in an outraged audience staring at a black, lifeless screen while livid cinema managers cried for his blood!

Probably the high volume of caffeine didn't help; an addiction that sometimes stretched to a dozen strong lattes a day. But it picked him up during the days when the night's sleep had been particularly rough. Besides the coffee he didn't have much of a method for dealing with the stress, only a gruff defiance not to be affected by it. But there were always the weekends where Marc could forget everything over a drink or two and in the melodic blur of a busy, local pub he could at last feel he was having some kind of enjoyable dream, not a coffee bean in sight!

The women came and went but it was never anything like what he had with Joanne. The two of them still kept in contact, though, but rarely more than two or three times a month and usually only via short text messages to see how the other was doing. On very rare occasions they would meet for coffee and catch up on each other's news. They weren't people to indulge in sentimental reminiscence and their conversations were usually upbeat and about their respective futures.

Joanne had since moved in with a new boyfriend and was still plotting her direction in life, having finished university by then. Marc would tell colourful tales of life in the fast lane of his newfound career and Joanne would just smile at it all and look as pretty as she ever did. After their seven-year relationship none of it felt strange or anything to be confused about. It was a friendship they were both pleased to have. The mutual consensus was that they had simply drifted apart but for Marc there was little introspection these days about what had really happened to their love or what might be learned from the split. These days he was enjoying a blossoming romance with *ambition* – a mighty stout rival for the affections of anyone!

*That's it, Marc, don't get sentimental!* A not unfriendly inner voice told him. *You've got to keep your mind clear for business, none of those emotional distractions!* There wasn't anything schizophrenic about this voice, since Marc didn't actually answer back and he wasn't entirely conscious of it in the first place. Rather, it was not unlike the subtle inner monologue that probably runs through everyone's subconscious mind.

*You've stumbled into the digital revolution and it's welcomed you with open arms!* The Voice raved. *But you've got to keep it up. Finish the coffee and say goodbye to Jo. There's work to be done!*

On the way out of the coffee shop a few minutes later Marc dropped some loose change into a charity collection cup and if an old lady had been coming in he would have held the door open for her and offered the most genuine of smiles. Outwardly he was the same cheerful, well meaning individual he had always been and as he and Joanne parted company she probably would have been hard pressed to detect anything different about him, except perhaps the taste he had acquired for dressing like a painter or decorator, albeit one with a liking for Tommy Hilfiger and Hugo Boss!

On a beautiful morning in late July the Quantum man turned up for an appointment with Alan Goddard, the Head of Marketing at Riverside TV studios in the trendy Hammersmith district of London, to check out their facilities. Over an initial coffee in its stylish Café Bar Marc explained the project and studio requirements but didn't reveal the artist, since it was still confidential at that point. Goddard proceeded to give him a leisurely tour of the various studio spaces, dressing rooms, office spaces and production galleries and it didn't need much selling. Riverside studios had a rich heritage, most notably for being the studio where the first British colour television broadcast took place in 1969, although nothing about it felt dated, which was not surprising as Alan proceeded to explain how the entire operation had not long undergone a major $1.5 million refurbishment.

"Let's finish off on the terrace," Alan suggested.

How powerful and important Marc felt as his courteous host led him around the impressive set up, treating him like visiting royalty. It was a feeling he had been getting used to. A minute later they were stepping out onto the River Terrace, which struck the senses immediately with its picturesque view overlooking the River Thames and Hammersmith Bridge. On the terrace itself were large umbrella covered wood tables with a few trendy looking types sat eating lunch and above them the panorama of the sky hung gorgeously like a specially commissioned roof painting. Marc knew how Alan must have felt having such a splendid property to show off. On many occasions as a real estate agent in New York Marc knew all he had to do sometimes was just open the door and let the quality do the talking.

"The terrace is a great place to unwind after a show, as well as mingle beforehand," Alan said, "you can book it for private use and we can lay on drinks and catering."

"Very nice," Marc said, "I can't imagine doing better."

On the train back to Aylesbury from London's Marylebone station Marc leafed through his leather bound notepad and applied his silver ballpoint pen to the next blank page, scribbling notes about his visit to Riverside. The key points to note had been the technical set-up of the studio, mainly the fibre cable connections it could offer for programme transmissions and the general lay-out of the building in case satellite uplink vehicles were required for any reason instead. He hadn't seen any other studios so far and the only other venues on his list were London Studios and the BBC, although he knew from Robert Young that Sony Music might already have a preference for Riverside since Bowie had played there before during a chat show appearance in 1999 and liked it.

As the lush Buckinghamshire countryside whisked by its rolling hills and picturesque villages begged his mind to think about nature and the oneness of all things and, of course, he did to some extent, but not in any deep, joined-up way. Instead the feeling came to him like a whisper, similar to the sound of a light breeze, not actually forming sentences but faintly evident nonetheless.

*Concentrate Marcy boy, there's no time for daydreaming!* The Voice interrupted, with just enough lack of rudeness to avoid being resented. *I know, I know, the revolution ... but once you've done this Bowie gig you'll have a digital big screen network spanning the globe, think about the potential of it! This is the way!* The Voice insisted. *One revolution at a time ...*

Back in the office Marc got straight to work whipping off emails to Julie Borchard and Robert Young with the feedback on Riverside TV studios. Luckily he had no other projects in the pipeline and could allocate all twelve hours of his working day to the Bowie show. The day typically started at 6 am with Marc rising to go online at home to see what emails had come in overnight from Asia, the Far East and Australia, who were between eight to ten hours ahead of British time. Picking up those emails early and replying before 8 am would mean the Sony Music reps in those faraway places were likely to read them up before finishing work on the same day, ensuring the speedy communication the project and his reputation depended on.

Strewn across the floor were sheets of A4 paper representing the different countries involved in the event and, with twenty two countries to cater for, the office carpet resembled fragmented slabs of glistening white ice at drift across a grey ocean surface. Each sheet of paper had specific headings and blank spaces underneath that needed to be filled in, starting with the country, then the city, then the name and address of the cinema and followed by the equipment and personnel required at each particular location.

There were additional pages marked "studio/production" and "satellite" and last but not least there was a sheet marked "5.1". As expected the digital surround-sound possibilities of the project was something that Bowie and the label were especially excited about, and became another ball to work into the juggling act.

He scanned through the raft of emails that were coming in from the Sony reps across Europe and, as with Asia, the Far East and Australia, some of the local reps already had details for cinemas they preferred to use. It was Marc's task to take over from there and negotiate terms and arrange all the technical elements, except in cases where a language barrier existed, in which case the only option was to advise the reps on what technical questions to ask and what to push for in terms of an exhibition agreement. He knew well enough from being inside the Odeon business what was reasonable and this knowledge was another asset that his consultancy services offered.

Several of the European Sony people had noted their local UCI cinema, in Rome and Warsaw for example, as potential exhibition partners. UCI were a good choice because they had done more than any other European exhibitor at that time in installing digital systems to show alternative content. The Bon Jovi success in the autumn of 2002 was a UCI exclusive and they had kept active since then with some sports and interactive games events.

From their European HQ in Manchester, England UCI was Odeon's chief rival in the UK in expanding the digital concept. But even with their substantial capital investment in the equipment they had been no match for the networking enterprise of Marc John, whose prolific programming for Odeon made UCI look pedestrian. Nevertheless, they were taking digital cinema very seriously and had a studious Englishman named Gerald Buckle spearheading their business development. Marc and Gerald knew each other by reputation and from various industry gatherings and the UCI man was probably the closest thing Marc had to a rival.

The irony and delicate trick now was that Marc needed to forge some kind of working relationship with Gerald Buckle rather than compete against him. Given that the Bowie event was an Odeon exclusive in the UK there was no conflict of interest in Quantum Digital placing the event with UCI on the continent and, strange as it was to coalesce with the enemy, Marc needed to take advantage of what UCI could offer. Marc telephoned Gerald to set up a meeting, being coy about the artist but upbeat about the box office potential. Gerald agreed to the meeting, no doubt keen to find out what his Odeon nemesis was doing even if it came to nothing. And, conversely, Marc could pump Gerald for any news on what UCI were doing as well.

For the 5.1 element, Marc had already made overtures to Dolby during the Cinema Expo trade fair in Amsterdam in June, where they were exhibiting their product range as usual. Cinema Expo was one of the exhibition industry's biggest technology showcases and a major meeting ground where shoulders rubbed in a jovial mix of business during the day and permissible vice in the evening. Marc was by then a regular face at the week-long event, having attended the previous two years. He would buzz around getting product updates from everyone and took pride in keeping himself fully informed, and usually there wasn't anything going on in the digital cinema industry that he didn't know about. But on the afternoon when Marc caught up with Dolby marketing manager Jason Power on the exhibition floor of the RAI convention centre the Dolby man had some news that Marc wouldn't have expected in a million years.

"I don't know if we can accommodate your project," Jason told him. "We're already working on a live concert that's being beamed to cinemas sometime in the next few months as well, actually."

What? Time froze. Marc's eyes bulged. He thought he had his finger on the pulse of absolutely everything that was happening in the world of digital cinema, especially when it came to alternative content. This was *his* turf. Who could it be?

"I can't reveal the artist I'm afraid," Jason said, which at least hinted that it was an individual and not a band.

"Who's organising it?" Marc quizzed, just as interested in who was pulling the project management strings.

"Can't tell you that either, sorry. Besides, it's not confirmed yet," Jason answered. "We probably won't have the resources to get behind whatever you're doing as well, if it's freebies you're after, although if you want to buy our kit that's a different matter of course."

No, it wasn't freebies Marc was after but buying the kit was not on the agenda either; something in-between was the deal he was looking to make. But if Dolby were already getting in bed with another project his room to manoeuvre was even more limited. A furrowed brow and clenched jaw realigned Marc's face and the Voice very quickly set about taxing him with ponderous anxiety:

*Nobody's in your league when it comes to organising these things, Marc, it's got to be hot air! But if it really is true and it happens before the Bowie gig it could steal your thunder, it might even put Bowie off altogether! You have to find out what's going on, don't let Jason off the hook, grill the bastard!*

"Is it just in the UK?" Marc pressed.

"UK and Europe. You can probably guess the exhibitor."

"That's the easy part," Marc said, knowing it had to be UCI. Except Gerald Buckle was no technical wunderkind and was certainly not running around the major record labels. So just who the hell was behind it?

Of all the companies sinking their corporate fangs into digital cinema at the time only two were really getting anywhere in terms of offering a full distribution service to rival Quantum Digital, and they were Boeing and Technicolor. Technicolor had not long set up a new, internal division called Technicolor Digital Cinema, or TDC, to manage their transition from being the world's leading supplier of 35 mm film reels to handling digital files. Technicolor had the most to lose from the digital age because if film prints were no longer going to be required they risked going out of business virtually overnight unless they could adapt and offer a digital service to replace their film services. Their first foray into modernisation was to get into the compression and server market by announcing a joint venture with a California-based vendor called Qualcomm, although their ambitious JV hadn't done much except look slick at trade fairs and court Hollywood with promises of a sustainable business model for a TDC-managed rollout of the kit.

Boeing, on the other hand, were leading the pack in the satellite business and was already the trusted communications partner for the likes of the US Government and major banks. They saw digital cinema as a natural utilisation of their proven, secure infrastructure and had set up Boeing Digital Cinema, at about the same time as TDC, to go out and win business. They had already scored a major marketing success with the satellite relay in the US of *Jekyll and Hyde* way back when Marc was first getting Quantum off the runway in 2001. But, like TDC, they had done little since except screen the occasional Hollywood movie in digital format on prototype DLP™ projectors in sporadic efforts to woo US studio chiefs to endorse their technologies and business model instead.

Marc had already met the top dogs at both companies and had sized them up as well funded sun bathers without his energy levels or vision. The fact that they were whales compared to Quantum Digital, a mere mackerel when measured against their annual turnovers and sheer resources, didn't mean they were going to pose any real competition. Sometimes a one-man band can out-play the biggest orchestras if the right chords are struck. By putting alternative content ahead of Hollywood product and aggressively mining the programme marketplace Quantum Digital had actually leapt ahead of both corporate behemoths. Maybe the empires were striking back!

*No, it can't be Boeing or Technicolor, they don't have people over here and they're pandering to Hollywood anyway. And it can't be Gerald, all by himself. Think, Marc, who else might be running around trying to sell the concept? Surely you're not done grilling Jason, he'll talk, work him over! No, don't. Remember you're still The Man, play it cool ...*

Marc played it cool and they left it that Jason would be in touch if the situation changed. It wasn't the ideal frame of mind to be in, especially since Marc's next rendezvous was the meeting he had set up with Gerald Buckle, his UCI counterpart. At least when they met at the Coca Cola stand – a popular, shoulder rubbing meeting point for quick business exchanges – Marc would already know that Gerald had a live event in the pipeline rather than his rival having the upper hand in surprising him. To have heard the news from UCI first would have been simply galling.

The bespectacled, immaculately dressed UCI man was on time for their meeting and found Marc already sat at one of the small tables around the packed Coke stand, sipping the freely dispersed soft drink and deep in thought. Not only did he have to come up with another 5.1 partner but there was now the very real danger of the whole damn thing being upstaged anyway. He couldn't help but feel a twinge of panic, as well as being frustrated at not knowing who the artist was. Maybe he could pump Buckle, although he wasn't known for being especially talkative.

Marc yanked himself into that zone of his and the two men shook hands. Gerald took a seat opposite and the opposing figureheads for Odeon and UCI's digital agenda spoke cordially enough. Buckle didn't have a problem with booking a music event organised by Quantum, even if it meant losing out to Odeon in the UK. After all, UCI would still bag headlines for hosting the show across multiple European territories. Marc decided not to reveal what he knew about the UCI live event, wanting instead to see how Gerald played his cards. For his part the UCI man, giving the appearance of being more like an unassuming accountant than an all-action pioneer, was predictably coy but eventually forthcoming.

"We'll have extra equipment installed all over the place for a live event we're doing just a few weeks ahead of yours, so we'll be in good shape to accommodate it," Gerald finally disclosed, no doubt expecting it to come as a big, jolting surprise.

"I know, my spies tell me as much," Marc quipped playfully without a beat being skipped. "Although I'll probably need a few more hours to find out who it is, I don't suppose you'll tell me."

"It's confidential of course."

"Who's setting it up?"

"That's confidential too, at the moment."

Marc smiled; what else could he do? Not long into the meeting they were joined by a man named Justin Ribbons, who was the senior Vice President for Business Affairs at UCI. Justin

was a little older than Gerald and carried himself with the air of
a decision maker and it was soon apparent he was the man
Buckle reported to. Marc had only expected to meet Gerald but
was fine with the inclusion of Ribbons, especially if it meant
speedier commitments being made. The deal Marc was looking
to secure on behalf of Sony Music was for a straightforward 50/
50 split of the ticket price, with Sony to cover equipment hire
charges where applicable. Quantum would oversee all technical
matters even in cases where the equipment was already installed.
It was all very straightforward and in less than two minutes
everything had been laid out on the table, except for the name of
the artist of course.

"He's as big as they come, probably bigger than whoever
you've got lined up in August," Marc promised, smiling.

"Okay, we're interested and 50/50 seems workable. When
you're ready to confirm just email Gerald the locations and we'll
see what we can do," Justin said.

When their meeting was finished Marc could barely wait to
jump all over his contacts to find out just what this other live
event was and who was organising it. So far he knew Dolby was
the digital 5.1 partner and UCI the exhibitor, which meant the
satellite provider and production company were still at large.
Surely one or both could be sniffed out on the trade floor and
badgered into discreet leakage about who the star was. And
since Marc had yet to pick a satellite company for the Bowie
event he set about his round of preliminary meetings with
broadcast companies with the dual aim of assessing them for his
own gig as well as trying to ascertain which one of them might
have bagged the mystery event.

A senior figure at NTL Broadcast, begging not to be
named, finally let it slip to Marc that they had been involved
in the discussion phases of the mystery event and that the
artist was none other than Robbie Williams. Robbie was
performing at the outdoor concert venue of Knebworth in
England over three days that August and it seemed the idea
was to do a live satellite broadcast of one of the shows to
possibly fifteen or twenty cinemas across the UK and
Europe.

Marc was stunned, not least by the fact that that Robbie's managers at IE Management had not come to *him* to put it together. Only a year prior he had screened Robbie's 2001 Cologne concert in the Odeon Digital Festival and had consistently followed up to keep the relationship warm. For IE Management to suddenly be doing an event through someone else was confounding as much as anything else. It wasn't as though the brand power of the Odeon cinema chain was anything to idly shirk and by then Marc took pride in being the golden boy of digital cinema. So just *who* the hell was organising it?

He wasn't finished with his NTL source just yet and, in what had all the hallmarks of a Cold War style collusion between secret agents in a dark alleyway, his NTL informant checked for eavesdroppers over each shoulder before leaning in close to whisper that *Sony Business Europe* was behind it all. Marc was puzzled.

Sony Business Europe was a big player in the electronic hardware market, being part of the Sony Corp but nothing to do with Sony Music, and whilst they stood to benefit from the entertainment world's digital adoption Marc would never have expected them to try getting in on the act to the point where they were actually behind live event project management. There had been no hint of this, no steady appearances of Sony Business Europe reconnaissance troops checking out the digital cinema terrain and now suddenly, out of the blue, they were bursting straight to the frontline with the biggest name in British pop! How so? It was time to get Robbie's co-manager Gabby Chelmicka on the telephone.

"Hi Gabby, it's Marc John, how are you?"

"Marc, well hello, I'm fine thanks, how about you?"

"I'm in Amsterdam on business and just heard it on the grapevine that Robbie is planning a live cinema event. Is it true?"

There was a pause but nothing so lengthy to suggest that Marc was unfairly probing, rather that Gabby was summoning the best tact to reply with.

"Well, possibly, yes, but it's not a done deal yet."

"Why didn't you come to me, Gabby?" Marc asked, trying not to sound too hurt or admonishing.

"This is just the way it worked out, Marc, I'm sorry," Gabby began to explain, at the very least respecting him with her time and honesty. "It kind of came together with Sony Business Europe and UCI. We know UCI have got the projectors and the hardware people at Sony were interested in putting an event together to promote HD production, they make the leading high definition movie cameras you know."

Yes, he knew. It turned out Sony Business Europe had recently sold a raft of their HDC-950 digital video cameras to a Belgium-based HD company called Outside Broadcast, who had been contracted to film the upcoming Robbie concerts at Knebworth. With his managers already primed on the idea of doing a live cinema gig the precise sequence of events that resulted in Sony Business Europe and UCI somehow cuddling up together wasn't too hard to imagine. It just hurt like hell that Marc had laid the foundation at IE Management only for someone else to take advantage of it – and for Gabby to let them. The Voice was not amused either:

*So it's Sony Business Europe and Gabby went for their pitch and not yours! Maybe you need to work on that laptop presentation a bit more, Marc! But wait, hold fire, this Robbie thing isn't even definite yet. And be nice to Gabby, she's just trying to do the best for her star.*

"Well, is there anything I can do, Gabby?" Marc asked. "I'm happy to get involved if you think you could use me."

*Yes, yes, that's good, slip in and get a piece of it!*

"A live HD satellite transmission to cinemas in digital 5.1 surround-sound is no piece of cake," Marc continued. "I'm reliably informed that satellite decoder boxes capable of decrypting those algorithms are not even past prototype stage yet."

*That's it, work some lingo into it. But don't stop there for god's sake!*

"Who's managing the project at Sony Business, Gabby? If you like I can speak to them and just make sure you're not in for any nasty surprises."

"Well, okay, it's a guy called Kevin Wakeford. I have his mobile number if you want to introduce yourself and check into it, I wouldn't mind that, Marc, if you're sure."

Marc didn't expect for a nanosecond that Sony Business Europe would entertain the idea of Quantum Digital coming into the project but that wasn't his objective anyway. Besides doing a customer relations job to stay friendly with IE Management Marc just wanted to find out how entrepreneurial this Kevin Wakeford guy was. If SBE were anything to be reckoned with one telephone conversation would tell him everything he needed to know. Besides, he didn't necessarily have to look at them as competition; if they were determined to stage digital cinema events to promote their product range perhaps Marc could solicit a few of their gigs to play at Odeon. Putting a call in to SBE could only be a good move and the instant he finished the call with Gabby he got onto his newest potential competitor.

Kevin Wakeford brandished the meaty title of Head of Digital Cinematography Business for Sony's Broadcast and Professional Division in Europe. It was one of those top jobs that can open doors, as it obviously had, but it was also one of those exalted executive titles that can make a man obese with self-importance. And when Marc got Kevin on his cellular phone he was actually hoping the SBE man would perfectly fit that characterisation! The last thing he wanted was to encounter a born charmer with one of those warm, fuzzy personalities that could make him a genuine rival to the smooth talking Quantum man.

Wakeford didn't disappoint. He was not in the least bit warm or friendly toward what he condescendingly seemed to regard as some inferior stranger quizzing him out of the blue about classified information, no matter that Gabby herself had passed along his number. For a man entrusted with business development Kevin came across like one of those actors in a corporate training video where examples in how *not* to conduct business are portrayed. Wakeford didn't even have the smarts to try pumping Marc for information on what potentially synergistic projects he was working on, and paid no respect to the fact that very real opportunities existed for his company via Quantum's status with Odeon. In fact he was practically hostile. No, in fact he was perfect!

All that Marc could conclude from the brief, frosty exchange was that SBE were putting together a proposal and budget for IE Management to consider and that UCI were getting the exclusive on it. None of the very real technical sensitivities, such as the level of compression to be used and how the satellite receivers would interface with the digital projectors, seemed to be very well researched but maybe Kevin was being deliberately mute. Whatever the case, it seemed the man had fallen into the opportunity rather than having carved it out of his own initiative and this was the kind of competition Marc didn't mind having.

*Okay this guy got lucky wriggling into IE Management but he's no dynamo*, the Voice injected. *You could practically hear him sneering down the phone line couldn't you, Marcy boy?*

But Marc had hardly been free of a few sneers himself, having dialled into Kevin's cell phone whilst pacing around the patio garden of the RAI auditorium stinging with hurt pride, seething that somebody else had dared to run with *his* ball. Indeed it had been quite a telephone discussion, full of pompous proclivity in equal measure on both sides. Of course, Marcy boy hadn't quite seen it that way. He believed he'd acted like a perfect professional, catching none of his own aloofness.

After the call he decided he couldn't afford to waste any time worrying about Robbie Williams or SBE. He was not going to gatecrash that particular party and had his own to think about, although he made a mental note to email Gabby when back in England just to tell her that he had spoken to Wakeford, who seemed happy being left to his own devices, so good luck to them.

The pressure was then really on for the David Bowie show to happen and when it was finally confirmed the following month Marc then had to contend with the possibility of Bowie going sour over Robbie Williams beating them to the punch. Or worse still would be if SBE fouled up and scared Bowie into backing out, nervous about the technology instead! This all raised the

question of how and when Marc should tell Julie Borchard and
Robert Young that another live cinema gig was being readied
ahead of their own. He couldn't sit on the news, it would break
sooner or later and he'd look all the more foolish and ill-
informed if Sony Music didn't hear it from him first. Those
sleepless nights were not about to get any easier.

# SLINGS AND ARROWS

On his last day walking around the trade floor of Cinema Expo that year Marc happened to come across the vaguely familiar face of David Pope, the business development manager for DTS Europe. DTS stood for Digital Theatre Systems and they specialised in audio solutions. They were the closest thing Dolby had to a rival and were number two in the cinema industry with ambitions to at least rank neck and neck. Marc had first been introduced to David Pope several months earlier during a live soccer screening he had organised at the Odeon cinema in Newcastle and the two of them had got on well.

"Hi Marc, what are you up to?"

"I'm on the lookout for a digital 5.1 audio partner for a potential live event," Marc answered, maintaining discretion over the artist involved. "You probably know I've used Dolby exclusively in the past but their man Jason tells me they've got their hands full with something else, so I'm a bit stuck!"

"Why do you want to bother with Dolby?" David asked, turning on his easy going sales craft. "That's AC-3 stuff and nowhere near the quality DTS can give you. We should talk!"

And talk they did. Marc didn't know what AC-3 audio was or what quality difference DTS could guarantee but Pope did his best to fill him in; with talk of kilohertz and sampling rates that Marc probably didn't need to understand as long as DTS could really deliver it. Audio was always Marc's weakest point in his understanding of the numerous, interdependent technologies involved in digital cinema but that five minute conversation with David Pope left him more than convinced that DTS would prove reliable.

They agreed to meet up again in London just as soon as the event date and full scope were known but the silky, relaxed DTS man left Marc in no doubt that his company would definitely want to seize the opportunity, assuring him that favourable terms could be arranged to ensure they were part of it. This was just what Marc needed before his return to England and he could now feel he had the vital 5.1 issue dealt with. Even if the Robbie Williams cinema gig went ahead it was still only planned for the UK and Europe, so the global milestone was still up for grabs and this gave him comfort that Sony Music and David Bowie would still want to stick with it. But he had to hurry up and break the news before it leaked and got back to them from elsewhere.

"I've heard that Robbie Williams is trying to get a cinema event off the ground," Marc told Robert Young from his Odeon office. "It's not confirmed yet but if it happens it'll be one of his Knebworth concerts in August."

"Live?"

"Yes."

"Where to?"

"UK and Europe. It doesn't match the scale we're working on but, even so, do you think it's a problem?"

"To be honest it could be, you know, if Bowie is seen to be on a band wagon rather than trailblazing."

"I know, that's why I thought I should mention it."

"Who's behind it? I thought you were the only guy doing this stuff?"

"So did I," Marc answered, "it's somebody at Sony Business Europe, looking for angles to promote HD cameras."

"I'll talk to Julie but in the meantime assume we're okay. Like you say, we're doing it worldwide and Robbie Williams doesn't compare to Bowie anyway."

Getting back to his emails Marc had plenty of following up to do with Riverside TV studios, who had recommended a company called Assembly Film and Television to produce the show. Their respective studio hire and production quotes had come in and Marc had to look them over and then pass them along to Julie Borchard, who had also been getting quotes from a couple of production companies she already knew. One of these was Hat Rack Production in New York, who had handled the production in Los Angeles of the Melissa Etheridge cinema event a few months before. Another production company putting in a quote was Blaze TV, a well known London outfit experienced in pop shows.

Blaze TV's budget came in the highest but their track record was impressive and they were no strangers to the set-up at Riverside TV studios either, where they produced a weekly Saturday morning pop show called CD:UK. Blaze TV's locality and credits ultimately won them the job but not before tough cookie Julie Borchard beat them down on costs. A well known British music director named Julia Knowles was attached soon after and, with the studio, production team, director and digital 5.1 partner all confirmed, all that remained as far as Marc's ground issues in the UK were concerned was the satellite transmission partner.

Marc was keen to reward NTL Broadcast with the contract so, to start tucking them under the sheets, he convened a meeting at the Odeon HQ to introduce them to DTS. The meeting included DTS senior business manager David Pope, Director of Business Development Ted Laverty and Director of Engineering Andy Tait. On the NTL side the business development manager, who begged never to be named for letting slip the Robbie Williams news, attended together with two senior engineers.

Ahead of the NTL meeting it had been decided between Marc, Sony Music and DTS that playing out live 5.1 audio in all ninety auditoriums was not going to be feasible from a hardware or manpower point of view, especially since DTS were supporting the event on a fully complimentary basis in return for the marketing value. The plan was for DTS to send out their 5.1 decoders to a shortlist of cinemas, exclusively for the event, and then collect them afterwards. Five locations were eventually selected, including London, Munich, New York, Paris and Zurich. Elsewhere the show would run standard two-channel stereo, which would also serve as the back-up at the 5.1 destinations should any of them fail.

The transmission of live 5.1 digital audio, together with stereo, genuinely was a very tricky feat; Marc had not been exaggerating when he stressed this to Gabby at IE Management. On the satellite transmission side it would require an encoding process that most broadcasters were not typically set-up to accommodate, and on the receiving end it would involve completely untested hardware and software which most cinemas would never have used or even seen before.

Marc sat there as NTL and DTS dived into a virtual foreign language discussion about the end-to-end process and, from what he could tell, it basically came down to having a specific model of encoder box at the studio to ingest the two audio feeds and then for a specific model of decoder box at the other end to thread the stereo directly into the cinema sound processor, while the 5.1 feed would first be routed to the DTS XD10 5.1 audio decoder box prior to reaching the cinema sound processor. Both sets of audio would therefore travel through the same broadcast "pipe", effectively bundled up together, to be spat out by their respective decoder boxes to run in perfect synchronicity with the picture. That was the theory, at least according to DTS.

Except none of it had been done before and NTL were worried that the DTS encoded data would encounter problems being bundled up with stereo and then travelling across the MPEG-2 private user digital satellite network they intended to use. This network was compliant with Europe's Digital Video Broadcasting, or DVB, standard for TV transmissions and as such was as reliable to use for the Bowie gig as anything else available – except a DTS 5.1 feed had yet to travel across the DVB platform and therefore posed an unknown quantity. DTS argued that they had already broadcast their digital 5.1 encoded data across similar MPEG-2 digital networks in Japan and across Swedish national radio and that there wouldn't be a problem.

"Sure we need to test. This is totally new ground after all," Ted Laverty expressed. "But the software, hardware and network issues are not really that complex."

The boys from NTL were hardly giving Marc the kind of nodding, comforting looks he had been expecting and suddenly he wondered if the digital 5.1 element of the project was going to be more of a risk than he originally anticipated.

"Chaps, is the technology really ready for this?" Marc asked. "We need to be putting a man on the moon if you know what I mean. We can't afford to be space monkeys!"

The DTS trio were quite adamant that a successful, live 5.1 transmission was absolutely feasible, while NTL were wincing as though there was a bad smell in the room. And now Marc was getting slightly paranoid that DTS were perhaps trying to take advantage of a big event by treating it like a giant laboratory for their product development. After all, DTS knew they could easily switch to stereo if they fouled up and, if that happened, DTS knew they could at least walk away from the experience having done a test rabbit job on some of their components whilst benefiting from a ton of free publicity in the process! Clearly NTL hadn't run into any of the DVB compatibility issues with the more established Dolby digital 5.1 encoded data, and Marc just hoped he wasn't going to rue Dolby's involvement with Robbie Williams any more than he already was!

Without resolving anything both sides promised to review each other's points and get back to Marc as speedily as possible on the next steps. By then it was the last week of July and little more than five weeks to go before the big night.

But the very next day, completely unexpectedly, Marc was stunned to get an email from NTL regretfully informing him that they were not sufficiently confident that the DTS 5.1 element of the project was technically feasible, particularly given the short space of time left to test and address any problems, and that they were withdrawing from the project altogether!

Marc slumped back in his office recliner and let out a massive sigh. This told him either that NTL had identified some very real concerns that DTS were perhaps not being fully honest about or that NTL simply didn't have the know-how or sense of innovation to seize a sensational opportunity. Or maybe NTL were happy just to focus on the Robbie Williams event, if it was still on track, rather than take on two projects at once.

Whatever the case, it meant Marc had to find another satellite partner and quick! Abandoning the 5.1 was out of the question. Even if the 5.1 was only reaching five venues it was still going to represent the first ever live satellite transmission of digital 5.1 to cinemas around the world, something Bowie and Sony Music were completely hooked on pioneering. As he flicked through his large, leather bound business card holder looking for alternative satellite providers Marc also had to pray that he wouldn't run into the same reticence toward DTS that he had run into at NTL, otherwise he really would be in a tough situation.

He logged on to the Internet and found his inbox flooded with dozens of updates from various Sony Music marketing reps, which meant finding another satellite provider would have to wait for the moment while he caught up with the correspondence. It seemed that several of the marketing directors had decided they wanted to hire theatres instead of charging, in order that fans could attend for free. The promotion would work via local radio competitions that would publicise both the cinema show and the album launch. It was a viable idea. The radio station benefited from having exclusive free tickets to give away to its listener base and Sony benefited from the equivalent advertising value. It was also another good, inventive business model to demonstrate how alternative programming could be booked in a cinema outside of the traditional admission charge model – assuming cinemas were not going to be unreasonably greedy with theatre hire quotes in the first place.

But as Marc read through the emails it soon became evident that various cinema managers were indeed going to be as greedy as they possibly could! Some of the Sony marketing reps had elected to approach the cinemas directly to negotiate hire terms even though Marc could have done this on their behalf. And as a result, particularly in Sweden and France, a number of mercenary cinema managers, realising that they were dealing with an international record label, were trying their luck by asking for exorbitant hire fees. The reps wanted to know from Marc if the quotes were typical, causing him to laugh out loud at the temerity on show.

He whipped emails back to these Sony marketing reps urging them not to agree to anything until he could intervene to clarify how those hire fees could be justified. With most theatres less than 10% occupied on a Monday night it was outright robbery for some of them to be asking for a hire fee equal to the theatre being sold out five times over! And it got even worse in Australia, where some of the cinema chains contacted directly by Sony Music were promising to take care of supplying all the digital equipment as well, without the assistance of Quantum Digital, only to have come back with rental quotes almost ten times the standard price – obviously having slapped a fat mark-up on the quotes they had got from local third parties!

Marc managed a wry, Humphrey Bogart-style smile and raised his cup of coffee in a toast to the pioneering days of digital cinema and all the mavericks and mercenaries out there! Incredibly, very few of these cinemas were considering the bigger picture of how the advent of digital cinema could foster long term relationships with the music industry and drive untapped new revenues. Instead they seemed only to care about making a quick, big buck. Vision was zero. Before finally getting to the equally important business of lining up a new satellite partner Marc also had to strongly caution all Sony Music personnel to refer *all* third party equipment quotes to him, otherwise the rip offs were going to be more criminal than Al Capone in his pomp!

Meanwhile Marc wondered how the Robbie Williams cinema gig was doing. But without having NTL in the sack he couldn't really tap them for any more quiet disclosures. And now that he was running with DTS he didn't really want to sniff around Dolby for scraps of insider news either. But then, out of the blue, he got a call from Robbie's management directly.

"Hi Marc, Gabby here ... "

She had news. Their event had fallen through! Gabby was vague about the reasons but was desperate to salvage it, saying that SBE and UCI were out of it now, and could something be arranged even if it meant a satellite relay reaching just one venue? But at that point Robbie's three concert dates at Knebworth were less than a week away and lining up a major

Odeon cinema at such short notice was going to be virtually impossible. Besides, the logistics would be equally formidable.

But the news came with yet another surprise. Gabby told Marc that another satellite provider was stepping in to take care of the technical co-ordination and that, basically, all she really wanted from him was a venue. What? Another satellite provider trying to grab a piece of digital cinema! Who now?

"It's British Telecom," Gabby revealed. "Do you know their broadcast services people?"

As it happened Marc knew all about BT Broadcast Services. He had worked with them when organising the live relay of the 2002 World Cup soccer tournament, via the BT Tower exchange in London, to a number of Odeon screens across the country. The reason he hadn't gone to BT for Bowie was because their services had been simply awful. There had been some serious technical glitches during the first of England's three qualifying group matches, when not one but two of BT's satellite decoders failed to work, and their digital cinema development manager, Gary Condon, had reacted with an alarmingly blasé attitude.

"Yeah, sometimes the kit doesn't work. It's one of those things," Condon had cavalierly remarked when Marc reported the fault.

Luckily Marc had a couple of digital TV boxes on standby together with terrestrial TV antennas on the rooftops as back-up which saved the shows from being cancelled, which wouldn't have thrilled the hundreds of loud, potentially riotous soccer fans packed into the auditoriums. The experience soured the relationship and Marc didn't really want to have anything more to do with BT. However, early in 2003, Gary Condon told him about BT's tentative plans to launch something called the U-Screen Network, which was another Boeing-style attempt to get in on the digital cinema act by offering satellite services and related technologies to cinemas in order to drive new revenues in a clearly emerging new media field. Gary wanted to invite Odeon to be part of a trial with U-Screen Network and Marc was obliged to consider the proposal and even arrange a meeting between BT and Odeon.

In April of that year Condon and his crew sat down with Marc and Barry Keward, the highly experienced Operations Director and number two man at Odeon, and set about their pitch. U-Screen were promising to deliver at least six live events in the first year of the trial and wanted Odeon to dedicate a London screen which BT would equip and maintain in return for a large slice of the admission charge per event. After the first year they wanted to rollout much wider. Marc knew their target of securing six live events in the space of twelve months at such an embryonic stage of the concept was wholly unlikely but he couldn't argue that Odeon had anything to lose by letting BT try their luck. Over that summer Odeon's Kingston-upon-Thames site in south London was picked as the first trial location to be outfitted with a digital projector and satellite kit, ready for whenever the first live show might materialise.

Except nothing happened. BT had woefully underestimated the difficulties in securing live events and it turned out Marc had already visited all of the record labels that BT subsequently approached and had made the better case anyway. The situation quickly became counter-productive, since Marc John and Gary Condon were actually competing for the same product with neither man wanting to defer to the other. But over the summer the U-Screen kit at Odeon Kingston-upon-Thames did nothing but gather dust and Marc expected British Telecom's flirtation with digital cinema to be short lived.

*So BT are hanging in there are they?* The Voice chuckled. *Well, maybe they've got their act together. Let's find out.*

On the telephone Marc found Gary Condon surprisingly reasonable to deal with, which hadn't been the expectation given the "may the best man win" attitude Condon had previously brandished, and each man seemed to finally appreciate that they might yet be good for each other. It even occurred to Marc that rekindling a relationship with BT might also be the answer to his own satellite dilemma, so sparking up a fresh dialogue turned out to be a convenient precursor to inviting them to the table for the Bowie gig.

But, much as Marc hated to let an event with so much career currency fall away, the time was just too short for him to ply an

opening at Odeon Leicester Square or at any of the other big
Odeon venues in the capital. Robbie Williams wasn't going to
beat David Bowie to the punch after all. At the very least Marc
had hoped to find out what had scrubbed the event when NTL
and Sony Business Europe were managing things, but all BT
seemed to know was that one of the sponsors balked at covering
the cinema costs at the very last minute, leaving NTL and SBE
with no choice but to abandon it, hence BT swooping down like
a vulture on a rapidly decomposing carcass.

"The Robbie Williams event is off," Marc told Robert on
their next call.

"What happened?"

"I'm not sure, I've heard something about the sponsor
reneging but it's all a bit vague. His management asked if I
could salvage it at just one venue but it was too late to pull any
strings."

"So where does that leave UCI and Sony Business Europe?"
Robert wondered.

"It leaves them all dressed up with nowhere to go I suppose."

"Hey, we should find out from Sony Business what their costs
were for using the cinemas they had lined up," Robert said in a
burst of inspiration, "maybe we can slip our Bowie show in
there as well and take advantage of all their preparation!"

*What? Is he serious?*

"Well, it wouldn't be that simple," Marc replied, "their event
is in HD and ours in SD. The formats are totally different and
their equipment is completely incompatible with ours."

SD was the abbreviation for *standard definition* and HD the
abbreviation for *high definition*, which in both cases referred to
the horizontal lines of resolution in a picture. SD typically had
625 lines in the UK, where the PAL format applied, and 525
lines in the US, where the NTSC format was used. HD, on the
other hand, ran anywhere from 1080 lines to 2048 lines to 4096
lines, depending on how much you wanted to spend on a digital
projector. 1080 was the minimum quality threshold for Hollywood movies but 4096, or 4K as it became better known, was
where the industry ultimately wanted to set the benchmark. The
Robbie gig was being shot in 1080, Bowie in 625.

"Can't we send out two versions, one high-def and the other standard def?"

*Patience boy. Kill it gently.*

"Yes, but that would mean shooting the performance in HD and that's not what Blaze TV have budgeted for. And even if Blaze did switch to HD at a cost Julie could live with the satellite uplink from the studio to send out HD along with a separate, down-converted SD feed will at least double the cost," Marc explained with legitimate reservation. "For the sake of a dozen or so venues in countries we've got covered already it just won't be worth it. We're better off sticking to SD everywhere."

"Okay, but do we have anything to lose by letting the Sony Business people make a pitch?" Robert argued. "If they want a big event desperately enough who knows what kind of deal they'll offer ... "

Marc had not been exaggerating the case against it, despite the Voice encouraging his arguments, but nevertheless he had to concede that Robert had a fair point. There really was nothing to lose in letting SBE in on the act to see what they might come up with. But Marc didn't like it one bit. After the call he let out a huge sigh and shook his head, muttering to himself how he thought he had just seen the back of SBE and now someone from his own camp was insisting on inviting them to the party. Unbelievable!

"This thing has a life of its own," Marc told Joanne over one of their occasional cups of coffee in Aylesbury's town centre. "I don't know what I'm in control of and what's in control of me!"

It was a truer statement than he realised.

"I'm supposed to be the creator of all this," he went on, "what kind of creator lets their creation get away from them?"

"You'll be fine," Joanne remarked. "Anyway, what happened to you helping other new directors?"

"Yeah, yeah, I'll get to it," Marc replied, brushing it away more than anything.

"Have you done anything about it yet?"

"I've got about a dozen tapes on my desk from newcomers asking for help with distribution," he answered, "when I get the time I'll take a look. I don't know, maybe I'll try organising a DV festival or something."

"And didn't you want to investigate what's going on at the UK Film Council?"

She was referring to how the UK Film Council – a government-funded film agency tasked with nurturing growth in the UK film industry – had, in February 2002, been exposed by some inquisitive members of the Conservative Party of investing millions of pounds in film productions in which six of their *own* Board directors had a direct financial interest! And then, just days after the story broke, Marc was attending a digital cinema industry get-together in central London, convened by the Department for Trade and Industry, where one of the Film Council's fund managers presented a series of digital short movies financially supported out of the cash pool he presided over as the Head of the Film Council's New Cinema Fund – which included a $2.2 million DV project that had been produced by none other than his girlfriend!

Virtually none of the abuses were being picked up by the press, despite the Conservatives getting their inquiry mentioned on the BBC news website, and the ruling Labour Party seemed perfectly happy to turn a blind eye to it all. The situation was crying out for a whistleblower and Marc had long vowed to speak out.

"Yeah, I'll get to that too at some point," he said rather languidly.

But he'd been saying all this for months. He rolled his tense shoulders and changed the subject. Joanne was turning out to be a good friend indeed, always making herself available whenever Marc needed to talk, which lately meant venting his frustrations in long outbursts. They had truly crossed over from being old flames to two people whose trust and respect for each other had sown a genuine platonic love, something Marc had never felt for a girl before. Maybe he wasn't finished learning about the ways men and women could love each other after all. Not that he stopped to contemplate this. He was busy trying to be a god in control of his universe.

"We've lined up a conference call with Kevin Wakeford," Robert cheerily announced down the phone, spared of Marc's rolling eyeballs. "Dave MacGregor's handling it, he'll be in touch."

Dave MacGregor was one of Sony Music's London-based marketing managers who Marc had got to know during the Melissa Etheridge event. The Australian born MacGregor had been Marc's chief point of contact during the Melissa project and they had gotten along very well, having watched the show together in Cologne when Dave travelled there to see first hand what digital cinema was all about. And afterwards they'd enjoyed a few late beers back at the hotel where they were coincidentally both checked into.

"I've got the details for the call this week with Sony Business and just wanted to make sure you could make it," Dave called to tell him. "We've told Kevin you'll be on the call as well, as our technical co-ordinator, although he sounded a bit reticent about having you on," Dave continued, "but I told him you were part of the Sony Music family as far as we were concerned."

Marc wasn't surprised to hear that Wakeford was feeling protective. After all, Quantum Digital was now going to be even more privy to how SBE operated than before; something that Wakeford couldn't have been too pleased about given that Quantum was considered a competitor. Marc suddenly found he could grin a little, where previously he could only frown. Perhaps the twist of events would not be as disadvantageous as he initially thought.

A few days later Marc dialled into the conference call line from his Odeon office and punched in the access code with particular eagerness. Kevin Wakeford and a colleague of his had gathered at Dave MacGregor's office in London where they were sitting around a speaker phone waiting for Julie and Robert to join from New York. When everyone was present on the call Dave basically handed it to Kevin to dive in and make his pitch.

Wakeford had already been briefed on where Sony Music and Quantum were with the project and he had come prepared to make his case having taken that into account. His starting point was to immediately attack SD technology as being poor quality and totally inadequate for cinema screens and that only HD solutions should be considered. His colleague ran a high definition production company called Ventura, which Kevin suggested should replace Blaze TV.

But what the HD pair had not taken into account, or perhaps didn't realise, was that Sony Music was already very familiar with SD technology from the Melissa Etheridge event and that Dave himself had witnessed up close, during his Cologne visit, how well received the picture quality had been. Marc always stressed that, providing the right compression and a decent video projector were used, the quality of SD in cinemas was actually perfectly acceptable. With the right SD solutions even regular home DVDs looked fabulous on a cinema screen. When this fact was pointed out Kevin tried to force the issue nevertheless, arguing that if an audience were shown standard definition and high definition in comparison tests they would demand HD every single time.

"That's obviously true," Marc chipped in, "but we're not in the comparison business, we're in the events business. When an audience sits in front of SD without anything to do with HD being shown or said about it they are more than satisfied with what they see. It's all about achieving a *minimum* quality level and working within budgets. HD is expensive and SD isn't."

Marc scored good points and before Kevin could punch back Julie chimed in to add to it.

"I don't think the audience even thinks about the technology, unless you're a tech head and follow that stuff religiously. We all want the latest and greatest technology but if less expensive equipment does the job and the fans go home happy why wouldn't we go with that instead?"

"Because there is also the matter of what you intend to do with the material after the cinema screening," Kevin pressed. "By recording it in HD you have the very best quality from which to archive it to DVD or show it on HDTV channels."

"We might get around to releasing a DVD or doing a deal with TV but then again we might not, that's not at the forefront of our considerations," Julie countered. "The cinema show is what this is really all about."

But Kevin was a persistent doggy, he had HD clenched stubbornly between his teeth and continued to shake it around, while his producer friend reeled off the numerous HD production credits his company had chalked up over the previous three years. It was almost as though they weren't listening to what Sony Music had to say. They were so relentlessly fanatical about high definition that Marc could even imagine them sat in Dave's office wearing corresponding t-shirts, one brightly displaying the letter H and the other brightly displaying the letter D!

Nevertheless, Kevin was a better business development manager than Marc had originally given him credit for and the wily salesman finally succeeded in convincing Julie to at least take a look at his quote for HD production services. He reasoned that if his costs could better those already supplied by Blaze TV for an SD production then why shouldn't Sony Music go with HD instead? Julie eventually acquiesced and handed it to Marc to comment on how a switch to HD would affect the satellite and cinema side.

"It would mean the technical costs going up," Marc began to explain, "HD projectors are three times more expensive than SD projectors to hire and the satellite costs, sending and receiving a high def signal, would also double, maybe triple. And forget about sending out SD *and* HD; that might lead some fans to believe they were getting a better viewing experience over others, especially if some people are so adamant about stressing the differences."

There genuinely wasn't much of a case for HD replacing SD but SBE had to be admired for having a damn good go. It seemed they weren't out of it yet. Kevin promised to get his budget over to Julie within days and the call wound down with Kevin probably not believing his luck at getting a shot at Bowie after losing out with Robbie Williams. The question now was could he make it count?

The proposal from Kevin was soon submitted and made its way to Marc – who was in for a shock. SBE were not just proposing to switch the show from SD to HD but to *replace* Quantum Digital as the event co-ordinator altogether! They wanted to assume full control of the satellite distribution from the studio as well as manage the logistics across all the cinemas, rendering Quantum superfluous, including shifting in Dolby at the expense of DTS! It was nothing less than a hostile takeover plot!

"This guy is some piece of work!" Marc said to himself as he took it all in with disbelief.

But the Quantum man had nothing to worry about. As he read through their budget it was soon clear why the Robbie Williams event must have fallen through and how there was no way Julie Borchard was likely to switch from SD for HD or replace Quantum with SBE – Kevin's quotes were astronomical! It was beyond avarice, it was a retirement fund in the making.

*You've got nothing to worry about, Marcy boy,* the Voice chortled. *This guy hasn't just shot himself in the foot, he's blown it completely off!*

The consultancy fee to SBE alone was nearly six times higher than what Quantum had negotiated and some of the equipment hire costs they quoted were so high that Sony Music could have practically bought the kit for the same price! It made Marc all the more disappointed that Gabby at IE Management hadn't come to him first about a Robbie Williams cinema event. He could have staged it for around a quarter of the general costs that SBE was working on. If the Robbie gig collapsed because a sponsor had balked at the budget, Marc lamented, this wouldn't have been the case if Quantum had put it together.

It was yet another naked, shameless example of how greed and short sightedness was hindering the emergence of alternative programming at the dawn of digital cinema. The necessary courting process was being totally ignored in favour of outright muggings. The proposal was politely declined and as SBE receded back to the drawing board Marc wondered if Kevin Wakeford would learn anything from having come close not once but twice with two of the biggest pop stars in the biz. Deep down Marc hoped not, preferring to see beaten foes stay beaten. And how dare anyone challenge him in the first place!

By then he was not above deriving a wicked sense of pleasure from seeing his rivals flounder and even toyed with the idea of calling Wakeford to wish him better luck next time.

But there was no time to rejoice at the tail-tucked retreat of Sony Business Europe, since Marc still had to ease BT Broadcast Services into the process, which was by no means a done deal. Not wanting to take any chances at such a delicate stage he also started talking to another satellite provider, Kingston InMedia, to allow him to jump horse in mid-stream if the talks with BT broke down at any stage.

Together with the DTS mob another meeting was convened, this time at BT Tower, to discuss the general timeline of the event and specifically how the BT satellite distribution was going to accommodate the digital 5.1 stream. Condon referred the hands-on responsibilities to an account manager for international projects and took a back seat role, monitoring progress from a distance. On the surface BT seemed okay about what was involved and, in direct contrast to NTL, couldn't see anything wrong with bundling stereo and the DTS data stream through an MPEG-2 satellite network.

But when it came time to getting a testing date arranged, along with a firm quote for all the services, the appointed account manager was increasingly hard to reach and forever making excuses about why she hadn't gotten around to any of it yet. This nonchalant attitude was not what Marc expected or wanted and it put unwelcome tension into the relationship at a critical time. The satellite contractor had to be locked down quickly because a major technical meeting at Riverside TV studios, involving all the technology providers as well as Blaze TV, was set to take place within days and a representative from BT would need to attend also.

When Marc was told that nobody from BT was even certain they could make the meeting it was simply not good enough and, together with the likelihood that their plodding lethargy was going to characterise how they would conduct themselves going forwards, Marc felt he had little option but to deal them out of the pack and quickly shuffle in Kingston Inmedia instead.

Secretly Marc wondered if BT had been trying to deliberately unhinge the project from Quantum's brackets in order to implant itself as the white knight salvager by making a direct approach to Sony Music at the last minute. The Quantum man could well have been paranoid but the possibility of an attempted coup was hardly dispelled by the fact that Condon one day gloated over the telephone that he knew where the production was being filmed and who the artist was *before* Marc had actually revealed that information to the appointed BT account manager!

*Let the slings and arrows come, Marc, it won't matter. This new frontier belongs to you!*

Kingston InMedia was not as big as NTL or BT but Marc already knew it wasn't the size of a company but the quality of its personnel that mattered. Fabien Robineau, the business enterprise manager at InMedia, had always reacted quickly enough to calls and emails, suggesting he wasn't going to fall into the same slack category found at BT, although only time would tell if his actions would prove louder than his promising words. The trouble was Marc couldn't afford to switch satellite vendors a third time. InMedia simply had to deliver.

It was a hot, mid-August morning when the core technical group gathered around a large table in one of Riverside's stylish office spaces, situated overlooking the River Terrace and accessed by a tight spiral, iron staircase from the terrace itself. The studio boss, Colin Black, was a good host, laying on enough cold drinks to satisfy anyone's thirst and facilitating the preliminary introductions. Marc then suggested that everyone take turns explaining what their functions were and in this way Blaze TV, the production sound mixers, DTS and InMedia all began to get to know each other.

The event was planned as a totally live transmission on Monday September 8th at 8 pm UK local time to the UK and European territories, with a retransmission of the recording planned for 12pm BST the following day to Asia, the Far East and Australia, with a third broadcast planned the following Monday, September 15th to Canada, North America and Brazil. Sony Music had reached the conclusion that three, separate broadcasts was the only way to run the show at a uniform prime time across all the cinemas globally, given the vastly different time zones.

However, with the event officially billed as *"Live and Interactive – an evening with David Bowie"* they couldn't have just the UK and European cinemas receive a fully live broadcast and the rest of the world just a recording of it – so the plan was to get David Bowie back in front of a camera to appear live at the end of the second and third transmissions for the question and answer sessions with the cinema audiences. In this way they were able to maintain the live and interactive element without Bowie having to perform the concert three times over. This saw Marc tasked with organising three days worth of satellite and cinema co-ordination instead of one, but he said he could handle it.

For the third and final leg of the cinema tour Sony Music wanted to broadcast the pre-recorded concert and live Q&A segment from a studio in New York City instead of London, due to the time difference issues and the fact that Bowie lived in Manhattan and would probably prefer being back there by that point. Manhattan-based Hat Rack Productions, who had done a stellar job on the Melissa Etheridge event, were by then already onboard and busy preparing for it.

The production for the first and second broadcasts by Blaze at Riverside was going to be straightforward enough, with the only specific pointers being that they needed to shoot in a widescreen 16 x 9 format in order to fill the width of cinema screens. For the first broadcast Inmedia determined they would need to park a specially equipped satellite uplink truck outside the studio because they didn't have the required digital circuitry at their earth station to receive the digital 5.1 audio via the studio's digital fibre cable. But for the second broadcast they could use the studio fibre since only the stereo channels were going to be transmitted. Their uplink would then zap the programme across the other side of the world and involve at least three satellites bouncing the signal around like a pinball.

"Even in cases where we're just playing the stereo the cinemas will run it through *all* the speakers, not just the left and right speakers on either side of the cinema screen," Marc explained, "so we'll get something you might call *surround-stereo*."

With surround-stereo the effect would be far greater and more immersive than just standard stereo, and some audiences probably wouldn't notice the difference between this and real 5.1 anyway. It was a plan everyone was happy with and already had its theory proven when Marc used it during the live 2002 World Cup soccer matches.

Ted Laverty and Andy Tait from DTS still had some talking to do with Fabien about how they intended to encode the 5.1 and stereo feeds for the first transmission, and a separate meeting was planned afterwards for this. But, together, DTS and InMedia broadly agreed it was absolutely workable and assured the production sound mixer, Tim Summerhayes, that all he had do was give them the feeds and they would do the rest.

Marc watched the boys from DTS and Fabien very closely indeed as they said all this, looking for any sign whatsoever that somebody might be rolling dice with the exercise, which the project could not afford. Fabien was handling himself well, showing the kind of knowledge and enthusiasm that had been woefully lacking at the bigger brands. Things were definitely looking up on the satellite side of things but Marc knew better than to feel any finishing lines had been crossed just yet.

The Riverside meeting wrapped up with all parties feeling comfortable about their respective responsibilities. For the well schooled Blaze and Riverside MD Colin Black it was more or less business as usual and the only real unknown quantity was going to be the 5.1 element. Afterwards, Marc, Ted, Andy and Fabien set about finding somewhere convenient to get down to business with that tricky audio stuff.

Directly across the road from Riverside TV studios was a sandwich shop with a few tables inside and a few buildings further down the street was a traditional, old English pub. The studio was quite oddly situated in a very residential area of Hammersmith away from the main throng of commercial activity and, outside of the cafes in the studios itself, these two establishments were the only places within a twenty minute walking distance to grab any kind of refreshment.

They chose to head into the pub, where a nice, tucked away table was able to give them the privacy they needed and, with not a moment to lose, DTS and the Frenchman soon got down to the specifics that had previously scared off NTL. Fabien, whose English was better than a lot of the people on the council estate where Marc had grown up, continued to show encouraging signs of competency as he ingested Ted and Andy's binary barrage with a hearty no fear attitude to it all.

Ted Laverty gave assurances that the special encoders required to bundle the digital 5.1 data stream together with the stereo could be loaned by contacts of his at Tandberg – a leading products and systems manufacturer in the satellite and broadcast industry – and that this piece of kit, the Tandberg E5740 encoder, should in theory do the job of bundling stereo with 5.1 without any temperamental behaviour. There were some other issues to do with setting up the equipment inside an InMedia satellite uplink vehicle, as well as some question marks over cabling, but provided a test could be done and quickly both sides felt the milestone was not a moon too far.

"Where do you want to send the test transmission?" Fabien asked.

Of the four European sites selected to receive the 5.1 feed Marc already had the Zurich location in mind for a test; the reason being that a local Swiss TV company, Tele-Zurich, was adjacent to the selected cinema and had told the cinema manager that it could downlink the satellite feed and cable it through to the cinema rather than Quantum having to install temporary satellite equipment inside the theatre's projection box. Apparently the TV station and the multiplex buildings were literally side by side and the cabling required was reckoned to be no more than a hundred metres. And they were even prepared to do it as favour, not a dirty mercenary among them!

Picking the Zurich cinema would therefore serve the twin purposes of checking the 5.1 as well as ensuring that the TV station could do what it said it could. The Zurich theatre also had a permanently installed digital projector, which meant Marc had ample flexibility in picking a date and time for the test since nothing whatsoever needed to be hired in.

Diaries were checked and sometime in the early afternoon of August 26th looked good to each of them for the test to take place. This would involve DTS getting hold of one of Tandberg's E5740 encoders, packing it safely in a car trunk and driving it to Kingston InMedia's satellite uplink station in Gerrards Cross in Buckinghamshire. It would also mean a nice, quick trip to Zurich for Marc to visit the TV station and cinema to personally observe how they went about their unconventional idea, just to be sure from seeing it himself that it was one hundred percent reliable.

In New York Julie Borchard was busy putting together a 60–second promotional film trailer to be screened in cinemas across Europe, including Britain, France, Germany and Norway, except Bowie had not been happy with the first version and Julie was now frantically having it re-edited so it could run with enough lead time to have an impact. The cinema poster had already been approved and was ready to go out, and Sony Music wanted tickets on sale everywhere by August 14th.

Bowie, however, was adamant that his hardcore followers should get the first shot at buying tickets ahead of when they went on sale at the cinemas and even ahead of whenever an official announcement of the show was made by either Sony or the cinemas. The star had a reputation for putting his most ardent fans first by treating them to exclusive insider scoops and nobody was going to argue with the wisdom of such loyalty. The way Julie and Bowie's reps at The Outside Organisation devised how his wishes could be accommodated would be for David to break the news of the cinema show on his official website, giving members around the world an exclusive opportunity to book tickets ahead of anyone else. David liked the idea and this was the plan they put into action.

Meanwhile the enterprising Robert Young was progressing discussions with the mobile network provider $O_2$ about using their platform to run a competition whereby fans could send a text message to a special short code number to stand a chance of winning tickets to see the Bowie show live at Riverside itself. The canny Irishman was clearly aware of the revenue generating potential of this and he planned for the competition to be promoted via the UK cinema posters as well as during the UK cinema trailers. Robert struck a deal for $O_2$ to waive not just the costs of their short code service but to also cover the bill for producing the UK posters and cinema trailers in return for getting an "$O_2$ Presents" credit on them.

This was a good deal for the cellular network operator since comparable, paid advertising in cinemas came at a high price. And, even though the trailers and posters didn't advertise any specific $O_2$ products or services, simply to have their logo displayed at the start of the trailer and in the poster frames outside the cinemas offered tremendous brand exposure.

Marc had needed to check the idea out with Odeon first, since the $O_2$ deal was potentially infringing the terms of contract the exhibitor had with its advertising broker, Carlton Screen Advertising. Under Odeon's deal with CSA the London-based advertising sales house had exclusive rights to all advertising and sponsorship placement and CSA had to be comfortable that the "$O_2$ Presents" credit was not a backdoor means of somebody else selling advertising and cutting them out in the process.

"I don't have a problem with that sort of credit on a trailer or poster," Carlton's commercial director Geraint Davies had told Marc. "In fact you should come to us first with these things because we're more likely to have potential sponsors than anyone else!"

Geraint's consent was significant because it indicated how new business models could be introduced at the outset of digital cinema whereby sponsors might actually fund digital programming rather than record labels having to be persuaded to part with marketing cash to cover the costs. Sony Music were still covering virtually all of the $500m budget for the Bowie show but Robert Young's deal with $O_2$ was nevertheless a fantastic breakthrough to demonstrate that sponsorship deals were indeed very fertile ground to plough, especially if the products and services of a particular sponsor could somehow feature in the event as well.

With this in mind Robert wanted to make the event even more interactive by allowing fans to send in text messages during the show which could be displayed on the cinema screen, and he asked Marc if he could meet a man called Jason Cooper at $O_2$ to explore the technical feasibility. Jason told Marc that as long as Blaze TV could provide a caption generator to allow a "text crawl" to be inserted along the bottom of the picture there was no reason why fans couldn't send in their SMS comments for Jason to filter and then upload to the cinema screen in virtually real time.

"I can use a fairly simple web based application," Jason said, "we can give the fans in the cinema a special number to send texts to and their messages will come straight to me at my laptop first."

The only hitch was that the $O_2$ tie-in was specific to the UK and since the text crawl would also feature their logo it couldn't appear across any of the European screens. With $O_2$ not competing heavily on the continent they were not prepared to throw in any extra sponsorship cash for the privilege of promoting themselves in those markets and therefore a way had to be found to display the $O_2$ text crawl on the UK screens only.

"Leave it with me," Marc told Jason. "We'll make it happen."

Marc was saying yes to everything. He wanted to excel to such a degree that the likes of Kevin Wakeford and Gary Condon would always think twice before saying they could do the things Quantum Digital could do. He didn't expect them to go away quietly and needed the Bowie event to put him in a league of his own. Being The Man was no longer enough, he craved the comparative dominance of an Emperor!

The battle plans were changing daily. At the MK2 Bibliothè-que in Paris, for example, within just an hour of Bowie announcing the show on his website it went from being booked to play on two, medium-sized screens to taking over the entire 14–screen multiplex! Tickets around the world were selling so fast that when the promotional film trailer was finally approved it was hardly needed. Right through August and even down to a week before the show extra screens were constantly being added to keep up with demand.

The process was not without its frustrations. For example there had been some serious language barrier problems, particularly in France, where Marc was certain a number of Gaelic voices down the telephone were purposely exaggerating their lack of English just to make an Englishman mad! This meant he had to call on some of the local Sony people to intercede, which was far from ideal since they had their own, specific jobs to do and this slowed down the co-ordination in ways that wouldn't have troubled a multi-lingual project manager. Maybe a course in languages was going to be something for the Quantum man to look into. Did any of his rivals speak a variety of languages?

Sony Music and Bowie's publicists had also yet to decide which cities around the world they wanted the live questions to come from. Deliberating over this meant time was being lost for Marc to arrange for ISDN line installations, making it more likely that lower quality standard telephone landlines would have to be used instead. Either way Marc also had to find local sound technicians to manage the Q&A sessions but he couldn't get busy with this either until he knew the locations.

But at least they were *his* problems to solve. Failure would actually be easier to live with than seeing someone else succeed in his shoes. Men in the grip of power can live with the most awful mess as long as nobody else but they get the chance to make it. Not that he expected to fail, of course. He was determined to take his chance. Indeed, the fledgling Emperor might have echoed the words of a figure in history who had similarly desired a sweeping dominion. "The favourable opportunity must be seized," Napoleon Bonaparte wrote in his memoirs while in exile in St. Helena, "for fortune is female – if you balk her today, you must not expect to meet with her again tomorrow."

But still he clung to a faint belief that it would all serve the revolution in the end, no matter if the intended sequence of events had changed. Surely they had changed for the better and this was his destiny all along. He was certain of this. And who was to say it wouldn't yet prove to be the case?

# - 6 -

# THE HI-TECH GODS

The weather in Zurich on the day of the test was clear and bright. As Marc stepped out onto the balcony of his hotel room to look across the street, where the Cinemax multiplex at Heinrichstrasse 269 was conveniently located, he hoped the obliging weather would prove a good omen. Bad weather was among the few scapegoats available to satellite companies to explain how a transmission problem might occur. The other main cause for concern had to do with the "line of sight", which meant the pathway through the airwaves between the satellite in orbit and the venue on the ground and whether anything got in the way, such as a high building or a solid structure of whatever kind.

Site surveys by satellite engineers using clever readers typically determined the line of sight well in advance, which left adverse weather conditions as really the only random element which could jeopardise a broadcast. And even then the weather had to be abnormally bad to blitz a signal. But this didn't mean line of sight issues couldn't suddenly appear where once they hadn't. For example, when BT's satellite equipment failed Odeon during the live 2002 World Cup soccer screenings BT eventually cited an unanticipated line of sight issue as being the problem instead of faulty decoder boxes.

"A long neck crane must have moved into the area," Gary Condon at BT Broadcast Services suggested when pressured to investigate the problem. "It obstructed the signal but how were we to know it was going to be there?"

"Wow, it must have been one heck of a big crane!"

"Yeah, it must have been," Condon answered.

Marc didn't believe it for a second, but if a monster-sized crane had genuinely, coincidentally positioned itself within the precise cubic feet of air space where it could intersect a satellite beam it had to be possible that it could happen again. The odds were against it of course. In a 365–day period how often would a construction project suddenly pop up and cause interference *and* have the merciless humour to do so *directly* after a site survey had been carried out?

But he was far less questioning of the satellites themselves. To him they were wondrous, brilliant inventions who performed their tasks with invisible grace and beauty. As he looked up at the clear blue sky from the balcony that morning none of the thousands of satellites that were orbiting the planet could be seen. Even when the stars came out at night the satellites remained hidden. Yet they were all up there, pulling strings not from behind the scenes but far, far above it. And they all had names too. These were not distant, impersonal beings; they were special, belonging to one of the greatest technological legacies in Mankind's history.

Ever since the Soviet Union launched the world's first satellite on October 4th. 1957, the famous Sputnik I, anywhere from six to ten thousand subsequent satellites had been jettisoned into space, some of them remaining active indefinitely while others expired from operational duty and just drifted aimlessly into outer space, lonely and doomed, their marvels forgotten. But every satellite was special in its day, when first launched on its own important mission after being reared and tended to by a loving coterie of scientists and engineers, feted to play some small but immeasurably valuable role in the development and definition of Mankind.

The original Sputnik satellite was no bigger than a basket-ball, weighed only 183lbs and took less than two hours to complete its orbital trip. But it was a feat of such ingenuity that the superpowers immediately seized upon satellite technology as the most urgent political, scientific and military research project of the day. The US responded to Sputnik with the creation of NASA in 1958 and the "space race" was on. On January 31st 1958 the United States successfully launched its first competitive satellite, Explorer I, and nothing would be the same again.

Satellites changed the world to the extent that Mankind wouldn't have known what the planet even looked like without them. For example, the US Landsat space project in the 1970s successfully transmitted back to earth groundbreaking colour pictures that were used for a variety of innovative applications including agricultural management, forest fire tracking and tectonic plate detection, as well as yielding other scientific data in areas such as tropical deforestation, ozone layer depletion and climate change. The satellite weather forecast industry especially took off to become a global money spinning enterprise beyond anyone's wildest expectations! By the 1980s and 1990s communication satellites were revolutionising every-thing from radio and TV transmissions to telephony and wireless connectivity. In the increasingly digitised age of the early 21st century the physical presence of the satellites was barely registered but their power was here to stay.

Marc was awed and fascinated by those marvellous metal creatures, with their distant eyes in space that could see everything in what had become a wholly scientific heaven, not a harp playing angel or halo crowned saint in sight! God was dead, usurped by these new, hi-tech gods who were just as omnipresent and even capable of doing things that the old gods couldn't manage in the first place, such as bringing people all across the planet together through miraculous forms of instant communication as well as liberate vast reserves of knowledge to the many when formerly it had been the privilege of the few.

Spiritual powers once transmitted through ancient mytholo-gical motifs and, later, the institutional faiths had now run into an age where the attention of the masses was being consumed more and more by the cold metal carcasses of technologies that had no spiritual dimension in the first place. Or did they? The old gods *had* to go. In the modern world, where cultures were now fully integrated and dependent on each other, the old tribal gods of the East and West were no better suited to the next age of the species than a pack of horse drawn carts to a sprawling metropolis freeway. But the question now was how were these hi-tech gods going to fill the void? What could they possibly *symbolise?*

The hi-tech god Marc John was praying to right then was a satellite over Europe called Eutelsat W2, which was reckoned to have the biggest broadcasting "footprint" across the continent. In his mind Marc tried to picture W2 floating mysteriously up there among the stars, bearing no grudge at being anonymous to the world and that under its soft, electrical hum and shiny, metallic skin was a rightful sense of majesty and unswerving commitment to duty.

Fifteen minutes later he was inside the cinema shaking hands with Sony Music's man in Switzerland, Roger Galliker, putting a face to a voice he had got to know well over the telephone in the preceding weeks. Galliker had been invited to come and watch the test and was already there with the cinema manager when Marc punctually arrived.

"So it's all set for noon?" Roger asked.

"Yes, if I've finally got the time zones figured out correctly!" Marc answered, alluding to a prior embarrassment on the matter.

Back in the UK it was coming up to 10 am Greenwich Mean Time (GMT) although this meant the local time in the UK was actually 11 am since they were in British Summer Time at that point (BST) which was one hour *ahead* of GMT. In Zurich they were operating in Central European Summer Time (CEST) which was *two* hours ahead of GMT and therefore *one* hour ahead of BST. Marc hadn't realised the difference between GMT and BST and this almost caused a calamity for those scheduling the broadcast in CEST as well as UTC (a whole different time zone altogether!)

The misunderstanding also extended to the Far East, Asia and Australia and the scheduling error had to be painstakingly corrected with numerous equipment providers, cinema managers and Sony marketing reps across all time zones, much to the embarrassment of the usually efficient Quantum man. The error had only been detected when one of the Sony reps in Asia had casually queried Marc on if he was really working on GMT even though Britain was then in BST? It was jovially put down as being "one of those things" which fortunately had been discovered in time but nevertheless it shook Marc up a little, reminding him he wasn't as infallible as he liked to think. "It seems I was out of sync with the whole world!" He remarked, mustering a little humour.

Before arriving at the cinema Marc had met David Pope from DTS for a quick coffee, along with a man named Patrick Engler, whose local company Protronic was used by DTS for service and maintenance work in the city. David had made a special trip out from London for the test as well and happily reported that the cables from the Tele-Zurich TV studio next door to the cinema had already been laid and everything was ready to go.

The co-operation and preparation between Tele-Zurich and the cinema, co-ordinated by Patrik, was first class and gave Marc a lot of confidence that DTS were going to prove more than capable of putting one over on their arch rivals Dolby. And the test itself was going to be pretty special since, if all went well, it would technically mark the first transmission of live digital 5.1 audio to a cinema, ahead of when the actual event could boast of it.

Just prior to noon, CEST, the assembled group came into the darkened auditorium and took seats in readiness for the test. The theatre doors were left open to throw in some light, silhouetting their figures as they eagerly awaited the mini-milestone. Marc had his mobile phone pressed to his ear, on a call with the Kingston Inmedia engineer back in the UK who was handling the uplink.

"Counting down now ...," Scott the engineer reported from Inmedia's earth station in Buckinghamshire.

*Get ready W2, you big, shiny superstar in space, it's time to do your stuff ...*

"We're up!" Scott declared, confirming the signal had blasted off into space where it would bounce off W2 virtually instantaneously with no more than a quarter of a second delay before hitting the Zurich screen.

But at the cinema the screen stayed blank.

"I'm not seeing it," Marc said.

"We're getting it here," Scott continued, meaning he could see and hear the test on their monitors and speakers back in the UK, where they were also downlinking the signal.

Patrik, David and the cinema technician leapt from of their seats to race back to the projection booth to investigate at their end. Marc didn't know what else to say and for a few, fazed moments he just held the telephone to his ear with his mouth slightly ajar. Roger Galliker and the cinema manager sat motionless in their seats and simply stared at the cinema screen almost as though they were trying to telekinetically coax the transmission to suddenly appear. And bizarrely Marc was doing the same!

"Are you still there?" Scott finally asked.

"I'll call you back," Marc answered, then hung up and left his seat to find out what was going on in the projection booth.

The projection booth was accessible via an entrance beside the theatre exit doors and the door was propped open with Patrik and the cinema technician visible inside checking a variety of knobs, buttons and cables. David Pope could only stand there, looking perplexed, his arms folded, waiting for something to be discovered to demystify the problem. Marc leaned against the door frame and tried not to sigh too heavily.

"It's got to be something at the TV station," Patrik said.

Galliker and the cinema manager soon appeared over Marc's shoulder with anxious expressions.

"What's wrong?" Galliker asked.

"We're not sure yet," Marc answered, straightening up and turning around to manage the situation, "we think it's something at the TV station."

"Oh dear!" Galliker replied gravely.

"I wouldn't be too worried at this point," Marc advised reasonably calmly, "the whole point of today was to test. It was never one hundred percent certain that using Tele-Zurich would work, this is really a site survey as much as anything."

"Did they downlink the signal okay back in England?" David asked.

"Yes, so it must be a local issue," Marc answered over his shoulder, then turned back to Roger, "I can call you later when I know more but I wouldn't panic just yet."

Twenty minutes later Marc, David and Patrik were at the TV station inside one of its equipment backrooms; a long, narrow, closet-like space where dozens upon dozens of satellite and data receivers were stacked in tall racks along the entire length of the right hand wall. One of Tele-Zurich's engineers had shown them in and they were now trying to identify which receiver had been used to downlink the signal. The engineer seemed to have forgotten! They narrowed it down to two or three, which were gently pulled out of their racks and checked over. They looked ultra-modern and functional enough but David and Patrik suspected they were missing a few bits of the software necessary to pass the six channels of DTS digital audio.

"But even if the audio failed we should still have seen the picture, correct?" Marc pressed.

"Yes, that's true," David answered, "maybe the length of the SDI cable was a factor."

In their tight huddle they speculated on how an especially long cable run can risk "dropping" the signal and that, ideally, SDI cable connections from satellite receivers into digital projectors are perhaps best kept as short as possible.

"Are we sure it was the SDI cable?" Marc pressed. "Did the TV station receive the transmission in the first place?"

The TV station engineer didn't actually know, as it happened nobody had been on hand to monitor the downlink on any of the station's monitors. It had simply been assumed that the transmission came through. Marc's forehead creased in a tense frown but it was no time for curt quips, instead he got on the telephone to Scott back at the Inmedia uplink station the UK.

"Scott, squirt me over five minutes of signal, we need to double check something on this end."

A few minutes later it was clear that the signal was not even getting through to the TV station in the first place, which baffled everyone. And nobody could blame the weather!

"This is strange because we downlink from satellites all the time," the station engineer said. "Something must be causing interference. I'll need a few hours to check into it."

That was fine with Marc, who wasn't flying back to the UK until much later that afternoon. A few hours later the problem had been discovered. Patrik explained that the interference had apparently come from a "peer-to-peer telecoms beam" that happened to run directly above the TV station. This P2P beam basically meant that a *horizontal* transmission link between two distant masts somewhere in the city was effectively blocking the *vertically* oriented satellite pathway. It was a variation on the line of sight issue except the P2P transmission line couldn't be seen the way a building or physical structure could be seen. Instead it was literally invisible!

"It seems this P2P link intersects the angle of your satellite beam and is cutting it off!" Patrik summed up. "Can you change satellites?"

Changing satellites was out of the question because W2 had the best coverage requirements for just about every other location across the UK and Europe, so it was hardly going to be scrapped just because Tele-Zurich had difficulties with it.

"I'll just have to put a dish on the cinema roof or otherwise park a downlink truck outside," Marc said.

"That's assuming you can get away from the beam!" Patrik commented. "There's no telling how wide it is or what interference it could still cause."

That was true. And it made Marc start to wonder how many other peer-to-peer networks he might yet run into. This was a totally new consideration. A lot of the cinemas had told him that their rooftops had a good, clear view of the sky for miles and miles around but, as he knew now, these inconspicuous, horizontally linked P2P networks could still stop a satellite transmission dead if they happened to intersect.

"Have your site surveys picked up any P2P issues elsewhere?" David asked.

"This is the first survey I've done to be honest," Marc answered. "I'm just getting to it now after being tied up getting you and the satellite distributor onboard!"

In fact he hadn't even contracted any downlink providers to start any of the work yet and was living a little bit dangerously. Kingston Inmedia had offered to take on the downlinking responsibilities for all the territories and take the hassle away from Marc altogether, but he knew he could get a better price per country by out-sourcing the work to local downlink vendors instead and his plan was to disperse the job to numerous contractors rather than give the assignment to any single party.

But there was another, bigger reason for why Marc wanted to separate the satellite distribution contractor and the downlink contractor and this was to ensure that no single satellite provider could claim too much credit for facilitating the broadcast. Otherwise Marc feared he would leave himself open to the threat that a satellite company might deliberately misrepresent their involvement and claim that *they* were behind the project instead of Quantum Digital. Fabien and his team may have been decent, hard working people who professed to have an interest solely in satellite services but Marc had already seen how the likes of Sony Business Europe and BT had tried to diversify into full scale digital cinema event management and push him aside, and he felt fully justified in taking precautions against creating potential, future competitors!

On the flight back from Zurich, taking even further precautions, Marc was even contemplating how he could divide the downlinking services as well, rather than give such a big job out to one vendor – since this ran a similar risk of somebody hyping their role in the whole thing and stealing Quantum's kudos. But he had options. He could talk to Globecast, who had handled the Melissa Etheridge event. They had proved reliable but were owned by France Telecom, who definitely had an interest in digital cinema, so he had to be careful not to accelerate their ambitions too much.

Also in the picture were T-Systems, owned by Deutsche Telecom, who were similarly keen on expanding their media services into the digital cinema arena. T-Systems had also played a part in the Melissa broadcast after Marc learned from Florian Ritter, the manager at the Cinestar cinema in Berlin, that T-Systems had installed a high speed fibre optic cable at the cinema for the purposes of experimenting with the digital delivery of movies and alternative programming. Marc contacted T-Systems and found it cheaper to have the feed downlinked at their earth station in Usingen and re-routed to the cinema via their fibre connection versus hiring temporary satellite kit.

T-Systems were very interested to be a part of it and cut their rates to secure the gig, seeing it as a great chance for them as well as Quantum to prove the viability of fibre delivery for programme distribution as well as satellite. The fibre worked faultlessly and a good relationship was forged. Marc would definitely be calling T-Systems again but, of course, the pie had to be carefully sliced because they were not going to be happy with supporting part credits for too much longer either.

And then there were the UCI cinemas around Europe that already had the satellite equipment, where Marc didn't need to worry about dispersing downlink contracts. But he still had to be mindful of how UCI would use the event to hype their own position in the digital marketplace, something Gerald Buckle would be doing not just to compete with Odeon in the UK but also to compete against Quantum in terms of attracting live events on a Europe-wide basis.

Marc didn't love the fact that he was adding so much prestige to the UCI digital portfolio because it could clearly work against him. For this reason he had already steered the Melissa show away from UCI in Germany and had booked it with a combination of Cinemaxx, Cinedom and Cinestar exhibitor partners instead. That must have rankled Buckle, who would have heard all about the Melissa event from industry circles, and Marc was probably lucky that the UCI man was happy to deal with him at all!

For the Bowie show the scope across UCI was eventually downsized to just a handful of cinemas, although this was not entirely by Marc's design. Gerald Buckle was actually his own worst enemy. Nailing the UCI man down on terms and contracts carried endless procrastinations and last minute changes that made life extremely difficult. At one point early in the negotiations, for example, a 50/50 split of admissions between Sony and UCI was verbally agreed, which Marc subsequently reported back to Sony Music, who in turn built the projected financial return into their profit and loss forecasts, only for Buckle to come back days later and say he'd changed his mind and wanted 60/40! It got worse. Even after 60/40 was reluctantly agreed Buckle then changed his mind again and said he wanted to axe the ticket split idea altogether and that Sony Music would have to hire the theatres at £12 per seat instead – double the usual ticket price!

Buckle's constant flip flopping over terms and conditions was making Marc look bad, like he couldn't negotiate properly, and he wondered if Buckle wasn't deliberately trying to create that perception in order to undermine his Odeon rival! Fortunately in Dublin the Sony marketers had opted to hire the UCI theatre in Blanchardtown anyway and give tickets away via a radio station partnership, which avoided any disasters. While in Warsaw and Rome the local Sony people managed to strike up a good enough dialogue with the cinema managers directly that the terms got taken out of Buckle's hands just enough that fair box office splits were eventually finalised, free of his intervention. But in several other locations UCI lost the event through that style of negotiation.

With time ticking down Marc couldn't take forever dividing and handing out the satellite downlink assignments and by the end of August a carve up was finally made between the French owned Globecast, German giants T-Systems and Teracom, a Swedish operator. The duties had been spread just wide enough that none of the major brands could overstate their contributions, while Quantum Digital maintained its unassailable position as the authority at the centre. Prices were agreed and site surveys were booked, with Marc trying to remain optimistic that the P2P issue at Zurich would not re-occur.

Back at that particular trouble spot the industrious Patrik Engler had managed to persuade Tele-Zurich to loan the cinema a satellite dish, which he found could be placed on the roof far enough away from the P2P telecoms beam to avoid any interference. This good news meant that the only remaining piece of kit the theatre needed was a satellite decoder, which

Marc knew he could probably cajole out of one of his numerous downlink suppliers who, mindful of future events, were all hungry to make a good impression.

For the second broadcast a series of "turnarounds" was going to be necessary; a process that involved multiple satellites being used simultaneously in cases where a single satellite could not on its own broadcast across a large geographical region. This time the European-oriented W2 would have to watch from the starry sidelines as Intelsat602, AsiaSat3 and Optus transmitted the signal down to the regions they were better placed to cater for.

Marc kept Inmedia onboard to uplink the second broadcast from London but again, just to make sure exaggerated credit wasn't grabbed, he assumed responsibility for organising the turnarounds and downlinks. In Asia ST Teleport was contracted to downlink the feed in Hong Kong and Singapore, Japan Telecom was chosen to downlink it at their earth station in Tokyo and re-route it via their fibre optic network and, in Australia, Sky Channel was brought onboard to pull the signal down in Sydney and Melbourne.

The entire, worldwide satellite interlinking process was no different to how a single operator like BT or Boeing would have organised it anyway, using local suppliers, so Marc was not taking an unnecessarily convoluted route. And by handling the turnarounds independently he continued to save Sony Music a small fortune in mark-ups as well as raising the status of Quantum Digital as a consummate distributor of global digital cinema programming. Provided he didn't foul up it was a well laid plan.

On a large world map, laid out flat on his office floor, Marc drew bright red lines marking out all the diverse angles the satellite beam from London would take in the first and second transmission. It looked like one of those airline destination maps that show how many cities a plane outbound from Heathrow could reach.

The third broadcast to a dozen venues in Canada, a single New York screen and three sites in Brazil was helped by the fact that all of the cinemas had useable satellite dishes as well as digital projectors installed. Most of these systems had primarily been installed to show digitally produced advertisements before the main movie features but were nonetheless capable of producing a high quality image up to HDTV standard, meaning 720 lines of horizontal resolution. A single satellite couldn't span these distances either but it was possible to get the job done by combining just two satellites over the western hemisphere, and their names were AMC3 and PAS9.

Marc completed the red line drawings on the map to give himself the complete picture of what beaming David Bowie around the world represented in terms of scope. It was sprawling. He stood looking over the map the way an ancient warlord might have stood looking imperiously over a giant clay tablet marking the breadth of an imminent, vast conquest. Napoleon would have been proud but Tolstoy's ghost would more likely have reserved judgement until knowing if Marc's emerging, digital empire would prove to be full of light or full of something else.

*It's all coming together, Marcy boy, keep it up!* The Voice relentlessly encouraged.

"Everyone from the President of Sony on down is going to be watching this, Marc!" Robert said excitedly during one of their regular telephone updates. "This could really take off!"

Other big names on the Sony Music roster, including Destiny's Child, Barbra Streisand, Jennifer Lopez, Simon & Garfunkel and Duran Duran, were already being touted as possible, future candidates for the big screen treatment and Robert clearly wanted to gain from it as much as Marc. The Irishman intended to carve out a brokerage role for himself by setting up all the big record labels with digital cinema, taking an executive producer credit and hefty fee in the process. Robert even started talking to Marc about forming some kind of partnership, with Robert selling the concept to the labels and Quantum Digital delivering the rest.

The idea of having a partner was interesting although Marc needed to consider what it might mean to his own empire building. It is not in the nature of power to enjoy being shared. But in the meantime he gave Robert every indication that teaming up and doing regular worldwide cinema gigs suited him just fine. After all, the cinemas involved with Bowie were ecstatic over how quickly tickets were selling and a lot of them were already chomping at Marc for more programming just like it. It wasn't going to be hard to establish a global network of cinemas and agree a fixed set of terms to screen regular live broadcasts.

His vision of a New Hollywood was flickering into life, a vision that saw the digital era transform the multiplex from being a mere movie temple into a multi-entertainment complex, where every week a live and interactive big screen experience could bring audiences together across borders, languages and cultures in ways not even the earliest, Old Hollywood pioneers could have imagined. None of it was futuristic. It was an upgrade waiting to happen and the whole damn thing was there for the taking!

"Yes, we can do it!" Marc told $O_2$'s Jason Cooper down the telephone, confirming that they could broadcast a feed in the UK to allow domestic audiences to send in text messages which could be uploaded to the cinema screen while the rest of Europe received a clean feed.

It would involve a caption generator overlaying a right-to-left text crawl graphic onto the picture without becoming embedded into the picture itself, enabling two versions of the programme to be produced. The production gallery would then feed the two versions out to Marc in separate cable runs for the satellite uplink part; which now meant a second uplink truck would be needed at the studio to accommodate what amounted to two separate broadcasts. $O_2$ agreed to cover the cost of the second truck as well as the caption generator and the neat idea was plumbed smoothly into the project.

The plumbing for the Q&A was not quite so obliging. By the time Sony and Bowie's publicists finally settled on the list of cinemas where members of the audience would get to ask questions it was less than ten days before the first broadcast and this was not enough time to arrange for the installation of ISDN lines. This would mean using standard telephone landlines, which wasn't really a problem since they had proved perfectly adequate for the Melissa Etheridge Q&A. The problem was the short time remaining in which to track down local audio specialists who could accommodate the work on such short notice *and* at a price that wasn't going to sound like a ransom.

In Australia the process was at least helped by the fact that the cinema partner, Greater Union-Hoyts, already worked with a reputable events company called Staging Connections, who were able to take charge of the Q&A issues at a price the local Sony office were satisfied with. But in some locations such as Milan, Paris and parts of Canada some of the auditoriums didn't even have a normal telephone landline to begin with, much less ISDN, and the race was also on to get local telecoms providers to accommodate several urgent installations!

At the studio end Blaze TV assigned a sound supervisor to the process of switching the calls and managing the box of tricks required to minimise potential problems such as echo on the line and, against the clock, Marc rounded up a patchwork of freelance audio specialists across Europe just in time.

Meanwhile, throughout August, Marc and the cinema project managers for the American, Canadian and Brazilian theatres had been holding a series of weekly conference calls in preparation for the third broadcast, together with Erin Williams of Hat Rack Productions in New York. The plan was to broadcast the pre-recorded concert from Manhattan's Chelsea Studios and then switch seamlessly to the live Q&A feed.

"A slight problem on our end is we can't show a 16 × 9 picture," Maureen Dennis from the Canadian cinema partner Famous Players told Marc. "Can you give us a 4 × 3 version instead?"

"But 16 × 9 is better for us, Marc," Jerome Merle from Teleimage in Brazil pointed out.

This was tricky. Famous Players were the only exhibitor whose video projectors could not display a 16 × 9 widescreen picture. But with over a dozen of their venues participating, right across Canada from Toronto to Edmonton, their technical limitations had to be accommodated somehow.

"Everything has to be broadcast in the same format and 16 × 9 is how the concert is being shot in the first place," Marc countered, "so I don't know how we get around this one to be honest."

"You can have 16 × 9 converted to 4 × 3," Erin injected, "that's easy enough to do."

"Can you show 4 × 3 at your theatres in Brazil, Jerome?" Marc asked.

"Yes, we have a menu setting that allows us to switch but 4 × 3 is not cinema, it won't look as good," Jerome protested, reasonably enough.

"I know but what choice is there?" Marc reasoned.

"Well, if you can send us a 16 × 9 tape we can play it out from our own satellite uplink station in Sao Paulo," Jerome suggested, "and then we can switch over to 4 × 3 for the Q&A at the end. That way Canada can take your 4 × 3 broadcast but we won't have to."

"We work with a domestic satellite provider as well," Maureen said, "so if you're doing that you may as well send us a 4 × 3 tape and we'll play it out centrally from Toronto and then switch over to you at the end in the same way as Brazil. It'll probably be cheaper than beaming the whole thing out from New York."

It was a good idea, especially since the Manhattan screening was going to run off a digital tape player at the theatre and not even receive a satellite feed until the live Q&A at the end. Basically if they could all start the taped show at the same time and switch to the live feed at the end, within no more than a few seconds of each other, it seemed a perfectly feasible way to solve the picture format differences as well as trim the satellite costs. And with a whole week between the first broadcast and the third there was ample time for Blaze TV to make the necessary tape dubs for an overnight courier to get them out to Canada and Brazil with enough lead time for a tech check.

"I'll be at the Manhattan theatre to supervise the show personally, so we can all dial into a conference call to synchronise when we start the show and when we switch to the live feed," Marc said.

Everyone agreed it was a good plan. The other key issue was making sure the Q&A was properly co-ordinated, although Famous Players and Teleimage were no strangers to organising two-way audio links in their theatres and with the highly competent Hat Rack Productions manning the call switcher at the studio, just as they had done for the Melissa Etheridge show, Marc dared to feel comfortable.

The Manhattan theatre was not originally on Sony Music's list and it was Marc who pushed for a venue in either Los Angeles or New York to be included. With Quantum Digital positioning itself as a global distributor of digital cinema entertainment the opportunity to showcase the concept and attract new business with such a high profile example of the technology in action could not be passed up and he pitched Sony Music hard to grant him the autonomy to stage a US screening.

"Even though it's not on your list it would still be great PR for Bowie and won't cost you a dime extra," Marc had said to Julie in mid-August.

Julie and Bowie's publicists gave it their consideration and couldn't find any reasons to object so Julie got back to Marc saying that, provided Quantum was covering any additional costs associated with the screening, he was fine to go ahead with it.

There was only one name in the US exhibition business Marc was interested in dealing with and that was Regal: the country's largest cinema chain. Regal was backed by the billion dollar fortune of its owner, Philip Anschutz, and had already blazed a trail ahead of domestic competitors like Loews and Landmark to become America's leading proponent of using digital technology to revolutionise cinema programming.

Anschutz had set up a sub-division within the company called Regal CineMedia, or RCM, which focused specifically on business development in the digital domain. Its small, dedicated team based out of Denver in the mid-west had risen to the challenge, pioneering a wide range of alternative programming including live sport, music, educational programmes, pre-show advertising and short features produced by the likes of NBC and TNT.

The success of RCM's Digital Content Network, or DCN as it was better known, was set to expand during 2004 to over four thousand screens covering nineteen of the top twenty markets, including New York, Los Angeles, Chicago, Philadelphia, San Francisco and just about every major US city on the map from the east coast to west. Regal was undeniably the alpha male gorilla in the digital cinema world and if Marc was going to beat his chest in a similar way he had to be playing in this kind of jungle *and* letting the whole world know it!

"We can do a deal with you, Marc," RCM Vice President Dan Diamond told him down the telephone from Denver, "but you'll have to hire the auditorium, we wouldn't do a box office split."

"Why not?"

"If we're going to do a box office split we like to have more time in advance for the promotion to work, otherwise we run the risk of splitting what potentially could be a half empty theatre!"

"But we'll sell out in half a day once news of a Manhattan screen hits the Bowie website," Marc countered.

But Dan Diamond couldn't be persuaded and Marc quickly realised the issue wasn't really the strength of the promotion, since this was already proven by the speed of ticket sales elsewhere around the world, the issue was quite simply money and its optimum extraction. Diamond offered a 441–seat auditorium at Regal's Union Square multiplex, which was located in a good spot at 800 Broadway, but he wanted $5750 as a hire fee.

"That's the equivalent of selling out every seat at a price of thirteen dollars per head," Marc protested, "when the average ticket sells for ten! And we're talking about a Monday night when the theatre would normally be dead!"

"We get very busy on Monday nights actually," Dan replied, although Marc had no way of knowing if he said it with a straight face.

Marc knew from having lived in New York for six years that Monday nights were rarely busy at the cinema not least because, especially at that time of year, Monday night NFL games traditionally kept a lot of guys at home glued to their TV sets, hugging beer kegs and cheering on their favourite football teams while betting on the "spread" and "over-under" odds with any number of clandestine bookmakers from Montauk to the Jersey Shore.

*Who's this guy kidding? Okay, he's a player, you're a player too, make some moves!*

"Would DTS be interested in co-sponsoring a Manhattan screening with me?" Marc asked David Pope, explaining the situation with Regal CineMedia but taking care to frame it as a genuine opportunity for DTS to share in the media spotlight that a well publicised New York screening could offer.

"We might just," David replied, "let me give you the names of our people in LA who would need to make the decision ... "

Marc could have afforded the hire fee on his own but had nothing to lose from trying to lighten the load. And with DTS there were no fears that they might suddenly try to reinvent their business to compete with Quantum Digital. Sharing the headlines with a well respected brand name in cinema sound equipment, who were also the exclusive digital 5.1 partner, seemed fitting indeed. Marc was soon speaking with Brian Caldwell, the DTS Director of Marketing, who liked the idea so much that he actually committed to it on the spot.

Marc was overjoyed. He had made his moves and got back to Dan Diamond with a real swagger in his voice to make the deal. And promoting digital cinema to the US media and content providers was only half the investment Marc was making, since linking RCM's vast digital network into his fledgling global schematic was also a major consideration. He now had a foothold in the US market with the biggest exhibitor out there. The empire was coming together nicely.

When all the satellite site surveys came back there was luckily no recurrence of the P2P problem encountered in Zurich, although Marc humoured himself that a whole slew of long neck cranes could still move into position at a moment's notice! But in reality he was feeling quite satisfied. As the final week before the big night counted down hundreds of equipment personnel and cinema staff around the world were all slotting into position like sharpened army conscripts waiting for the whistle command to set a glorious charge into motion.

Not that there weren't a few more last minute requests to deal with. With less than a week to go one of Sony Music's London-based executives, Sharon Addison, tracked him down to say she wanted to hire a restaurant in London for Sony executives to watch the show over a special dinner, so could he find time to arrange for all the necessary equipment to be installed? At about the same time the Sony Music office in Berlin decided they wanted a nightclub in Düsseldorf to take the broadcast as well, so could Marc please see to this too?

"Give me five minutes and I'll have it all dealt with," Marc would quip.

It took a bit longer than five minutes but Club 3000 in Düsseldorf and the restaurant at 5 Cavendish Square in London got what they needed. The only negative fallout from such last minute requests was that Marc wasn't able to concentrate on sending out invitations to the US media and content industry for the Manhattan screening. Instead he had to hope for some breathing space the following week where he could perhaps make some more of his moves before flying out to New York on Friday, September 12th. But he refused to grumble. Did Clark Kent ever grumble, he asked himself?

There was just no switching off, no private time that was off limits. It wasn't uncommon for calls to come in from Julie or Robert in New York as late as midnight and during the final week he even told the people not to worry waking him at 3 am if they needed to. One unconventionally timed call actually came in on the very weekend before the big day itself, close to 11 pm on the Friday, just when Marc had felt safe to crack open a bottle of Merlot and chill down.

"Hi Marc, it's Jean, Julie's assistant, Julie needs to speak to you urgently. Can I put you through?"

It sounded ominous and he thought about putting the kettle on quickly in case his powers of sobriety were going to be called upon.

"Er, yes, of course," he said, deciding that a healthy gulp of the red stuff might do just as well.

Ten seconds later:

"Marc, it's Julie, I've got some nut on the phone claiming he's the CEO of Palace Cinemas in Europe and he's threatening to downlink the signal in Budapest!"

Hungary had not been a target market for the album and a deal hadn't been done in Budapest but this hadn't stopped the man in question from wanting to show the programme at his cinema regardless, which apparently already had all the necessary digital equipment installed to take the feed and show it.

"He's been yelling down the telephone and going crazy, it's unbelievable," Julie went on, "I've got him on the other line right now, if I patch you into a three-way call can you help me explain that he's not authorised to downlink the signal and basically get him to back off?"

Marc was game enough. As serious as the situation sounded it had just as much potential to be mildly amusing and with Marc mellowing out with a fine, fruity bouquet it was probably as good a moment as any to tackle a wild man.

"Sure, patch me in," Marc said, topping up his glass.

Julie wasn't kidding. The man, who introduced himself as VJ Maury, was explosive to say the least and Marc wondered if he might have tipped back the odd spirit himself given the raucous tirade he was spewing down the line. Marc had never heard anything like it before and half wondered if this was Julie's idea of a stress-busting joke! But it was no joke. Maury bellowed what his lofty credentials were and insisted that his cinema in Budapest should be allowed to show the gig; certain that they'd sell out.

"The decision to participate in the broadcast has to come from Sony's side," Marc calmly injected, "just because a cinema has the equipment doesn't automatically mean you can show it. Budapest isn't on the list, so you can't show it."

But the hyperbolic rant continued and Maury threatened to downlink the signal with or without permission. It turned out he had the satellite co-ordinates – the sequence of digits that had to be programmed into the satellite receivers in order for the signal to be received and decrypted – from the cinema manager at the Palace cinema in Prague, who were on the official list. All

Budapest needed to do was programme the digits into their satellite decoder and they'd get the signal as big and beautiful as everyone else. It was definitely a problem. But there was no reasoning with the supposed CEO and finally Julie urged Marc that they should just hang up and confer privately.

So they hung up, cutting off Maury's incredible venom the way a swift chop of an axe would take the head off a hissing snake. Moments later Julie called Marc back and apologised for having interrupted his evening with such an unsettling call. Marc hadn't minded, it was all part of the job and in a way it flattered the importance of the event that a man could get so upset about one of his cinemas being left out!

Nevertheless, something had to be done to ensure that the Budapest cinema didn't go ahead and illegally downlink the transmission. The only option was to change the satellite co-ordinates. Marc had emailed the precious digits to all the cinemas and satellite partners earlier that week and didn't know if it was possible to change them at such a late stage, especially with it being the weekend. And even if it was possible there would also be the task of making sure all the relevant people knew about the new co-ordinates in time for them to be programmed.

Marc left it that he would talk to Inmedia in the morning to see what was feasible. Julie and Robert were due to arrive in England over the weekend and be at Riverside TV studios during the Sunday when a lot of setting up and testing was taking place. Marc planned to be there too so they agreed to talk again when they met at the studio.

In the meantime Marc had the rest of Friday night to finish his wine and all of Saturday to worry about the Budapest dilemma. The call with VJ Maury hadn't shaken him up that much and wouldn't have done so even without the buffer of the red stuff. Nothing anybody could do or say had much chance of affecting him at that point. By now he was permanently "in the zone" – cut off from emotion and functioning less like a man now and more like a machine. And that suited him just fine. Machines, after all, were now his best friends.

# 7

# THE MACHINE

On Sunday Marc planned to arrive at Riverside studios by the mid-afternoon and spent the morning collating and printing out an information sheet detailing all the personnel at each location. In his highly methodical, machine-like manner he had switched on his laptop to get to work as though they were two components of the same engine. And where the Voice was once heard in whispering human tones it now took on the distinctive, tinny monotone of sounding electronically processed.

*Awake. Coffee. Three cup limit. Fingers on keyboard. Focus. Proceed.*

Fortunately it had been possible to change the satellite co-ordinates. The Inmedia account manager handling the satellite space segment booking, Lowri Davies, had been good enough to call Marc back after he left a message on her cellular voice mail on Saturday afternoon. Lowri had been playing football for an amateur girls team when he called but afterwards she wasted no time getting on to Eutelsat, who owned and operated W2, to have new co-ordinates assigned. Marc then spent the rest of Saturday forwarding the revised digits to all the cinemas and satellite vendors, with a specifically worded provision that only people receiving the information directly from Quantum Digital were authorised to downlink and decrypt the signal. Under this provision the likes of VJ Maury would be guilty of piracy if an attempt was made to take the feed in Budapest.

On the train ride into London the spiritual whispers radiating from the open countryside were struggling to register an impact, since all Marc John wanted the rural Buckinghamshire countryside to do now was not affect his mobile network service, which remote greenbelt areas of the country were frustratingly inclined to do. When the network coverage did occasionally drop Marc would inevitably gaze out the window and nature would have its chance. But then the signal would come alive again and he would be back making calls. Throughout the fifty-five minute journey it alternated like this, nature versus network, practically a tussle; a duel for the soul.

At Marylebone station in London he dived into a taxi rather than take the tube, needing to keep his mobile phone signal as active as possible. He had a small rucksack with him with two changes of clothes, as well as his laptop case, and the plan was to go straight to Riverside studios for the setting up and testing and check into the hotel he had booked for two nights when the day ended much later, probably at around 1 am.

As the London black cab cruised into the Hammersmith area and came along Crisp Road towards the studio Marc could see two huge vehicles already parked along the right hand side street next to the building. These were the sound mixing trucks but looked more like giant movie star trailers. The sight of them filled Marc with nervous excitement as he jumped out of the taxi and headed into the building, stopping at the reception desk to collect his Access All Areas name badge before heading across a communal bar area and down a corridor toward the production office.

The production office was a tight but functional room roughly six metres square with four or five smallish desks spaced about, one of which had been cleared for Marc's use. There was also a refrigerator, a widescreen plasma TV and, against one of the walls, a pile of bags, backpacks and other personal items were stacked high in a kind of temporary storage heap. Marc added his own backpack to it and set about unpacking his laptop on top of the free desk. He genially mouthed the word "Hello" to the members of the Blaze TV production staff who were already there but they were all far too engrossed on telephone calls to acknowledge him back.

Rather awkwardly Marc fumbled around behind his desk to connect his laptop to a phone jack in order to access the

Internet, only to find he couldn't get an outside line. He looked around with an expression that begged for help but the Blaze TV people were still too busy on their telephone calls to come to his aid. They were in full flow of being machines themselves and he was in their hub now – an epicentre of activity where everything really did need to work like a sophisticated piece of engineering. The atmosphere should have been ideal for him but a little bit of the old human world wouldn't have gone amiss right then either. But he couldn't have it both ways and finally he turned back and just sat there with a face like a frozen, crashed PC screen.

*Task incomplete. Assistance currently unavailable. Exercise patience.*

"You have to dial nine first," a familiar sounding voice advised.

It was Colin Black, the studio's amiable MD, who had popped his head around the door to check if Marc had arrived and was settling in okay. Colin's trademark smile rebooted his spirits and was just the human touch he needed to feel less like the new kid in class on the first day of school. The dial nine trick worked and Marc logged on without a problem.

"Is there anything else you need?" Colin asked.

Marc had to find Kevin Duff, the sound supervisor manning the Q&A switcher, and then locate where the satellite truck was parked to check if the special digital equipment, the DTS CAE5 and Tandberg E5740 encoders, had been fitted okay. Colin led Marc into Studio 1 via a private entrance, which was directly next door to the production office, to show him how to get to the production galleries and sound booths, where Kevin could be found. These were situated on the next floor up and accessed via a discreet flight of steps welded to the rear wall of the studio itself.

In front of this straight, steep rung of steps the Blaze TV crew hands were busy unpacking all sorts of equipment, setting up camera platforms and constructing the stage. Studio 1 was a big space, roughly twenty one metres square, with high ceilings and huge loading bay doors that made it look like an aircraft hangar. All four walls were painted completely black, which Marc guessed must have been the best colour scheme for a studio space for whatever reason, and cables were strewn in every direction across the black satin finished floor, making it look like a bowl of giant, multi-coloured spaghetti had been tipped in from the roof!

Marc assured Colin he'd be okay at that point and let the studio chief get back to other things; then skipped up the stairs to find Kevin Duff in one of the sound booths.

"Here's the list of Q&A operators and the numbers to dial into," Marc said, handing Kevin a contact sheet.

The two-way audio links would involve Kevin dialling into a dedicated landline number at each cinema, getting them all onto one call via something called a telephone bridge and then switching from one to the other in the predetermined sequence in which the questions would be asked. All the cinemas would get to hear the Q&A and Bowie would have an earpiece fitted to hear the questions himself whilst answering over satellite directly to the camera. The novelty of it had been the most enjoyable aspect of the Melissa Etheridge event, as audiences marvelled at seeing the giant face of a music star talking back to them on the cinema screen despite being half way across the planet, and everyone on the Bowie show was just as excited that his fans were in for the same treat.

Next Marc caught up with Andy Tait from DTS, who was walking back and forth through the narrow gangways at the rear of the building between the side street on the right, where the sound mixing trucks were parked, and the side street on the left, where the satellite uplink trucks were due to be positioned. The distance separating the streets was approximately fifty metres, something Andy looked concerned about.

"I'm worried about the sound cables reaching the satellite trucks!" Andy said. "I didn't realise the trucks were going to be on opposite sides of the building!"

But there hadn't been much choice in the matter. Kingston Inmedia's satellite site survey weeks earlier had established that the uplink dishes on top of their trucks would not be able to get a clear line of sight to W2 from the right side of the building, only from the left. And it turned out the sound trucks couldn't be parked anywhere but down the right hand side of the building, since this provided the best access into Studio 1 and the production gallery via the loading bay doors. It wasn't unusual for sound trucks to accommodate long cable runs but Andy was more concerned about whether a route through the back of the building could be found for the cables to be securely laid, since there was no straightforward or easy pathway to cross from the right side of the building to the left.

"When does all this start getting easy?" Marc asked wryly.

"When it's over," Andy replied with matching wit.

Eventually Andy and one of the sound truck crew managed to thread the cables through the building via an elaborate trail that took most of the afternoon to navigate. It all looked far more precarious than anyone would ideally have wanted.

"Don't worry," Andy said to Marc, "it should still work."

"Should?" Marc fretted.

"Hey, this is rock 'n' roll!" Andy exclaimed with a smile.

Meanwhile the satellite truck had arrived and had backed up against a side entrance on the left of the building which led directly onto the studio's River Terrace. It was from this vantage point, with a clear view of the sky, that the best line of sight to W2 could be found. The proximity was also good from the standpoint of laying the production cables out from the studio. All that had to be done was for the feeds to be laid unobtrusively across the terrace deck to run into the back of the trucks.

With everything hooked up by 6 pm it was then a waiting game for the scheduled satellite tests to commence, which were not due until 9 pm BST for the UK and European cinemas and 11 pm BST for the Far East, Japan and Australia, given the forward time difference of the latter countries. In the meantime Blaze TV had plenty to do with the stage dressing and lighting design, which long-standing Bowie lighting specialist Tom Kenny took command of.

Marc's triple A pass meant he was able to wander around at leisure and take it all in, which he did with a mixture of fascination and awe. The buzz was that David Bowie himself was planning to drop by to see how things were progressing and every time a slim, blond, nattily dressed figure appeared somewhere in the building heads would turn and hushed tones would flutter wondering if it was *him.*

Marc had never met a superstar before and catching a glimpse of Bowie was something that intrigued him too. What would it do to him, to see and maybe even be introduced to a music legend whose imminent performance was actually all of his making? David Bowie probably wouldn't have looked twice at him but Marc didn't mind that. His ego had been getting plenty of massages – and power doesn't always have to make a man famous to work its black magic. But he did want to meet Bowie, to shake his hand and see if any physiological changes did in fact occur when ordinary people met stars.

The effect wasn't likely to be one of unbridled delirium since Marc was not exactly a hardcore Bowie fan, although the star's remarkable legacy over nearly four decades hadn't escaped him either. Christmas was not Christmas without regular TV and radio air play of *Peace on Earth/Little Drummer Boy,* Bowie's classic duet with legendary old school crooner Bing Crosby, and when he first started getting into music at around the age of thirteen, digging through his mother's vinyl record collection in the days before compact disc, Bowie's 1973 hit *Life on Mars* had been one of the first songs he liked enough to play over and over again.

Later as a movie lover in his teens Marc was surprised to come across Bowie in a range of interesting, offbeat films like *The Man Who Fell to Earth* and *Merry Christmas, Mr Lawrence.* And in 1986 the Aylesbury cinema buff was one of the few who bothered to see the underrated Brit flick *Absolute Beginners,* which Bowie starred in along with singing the title song. He didn't make a point of catching every Bowie movie but especially liked his beautifully nuanced portrayal of pop art godfather Andy Warhol in 1996's *Basquiat,* a worthy biopic of the gifted, famed and ultimately doomed 1980s New York graffiti artist Jean-Michel Basquiat.

It seemed no matter what the decade Bowie always seemed to pop up somewhere in the cultural spectrum, unfailingly doing his own thing regardless of populist taste, satisfying his existing fans and almost always winning over new ones. And when he had to be commercial or mainstream he seemed to turn it on like a tap. One of the big songs Marc remembered from the 1980s was Bowie's worldwide hit *Let's Dance* and when the Live Aid concert of 1985 made history David Bowie's stint was among the most memorable. Bowie was certainly the best dressed!

So even as a relative non-fan David Bowie had penetrated Marc John's taste bubble and enriched it in a way that no other music star could match. And all this without Marc being influenced by any of Bowie's more celebrated career innovations, such as the glam rock glory of Ziggy Stardust or his cool metamorphosis into The Thin White Duke during the 1970s, a decade which culminated with Bowie restyling himself yet again to become a synthesiser pioneer during a three-year hiatus in Berlin, out of which the New Wave music of the 1980s would most likely not have flourished. Overall the star had sold an astonishing 136,000,000 records over a celestial forty years of rock and reinvention. Outside of Elvis Presley and The Beatles cultural influences didn't get much bigger than David Bowie and, even at the turn of the 21st century, he was still *there,* as alive and vital to the scene as anyone.

Julie Borchard and Robert Young were in good, relaxed spirits when they arrived at the studio early that evening. It was Marc's first time seeing them in several months and, after having communicated so much with them by email and telephone, it was quite strange relating to them in person again. Julie was relieved to hear that the satellite co-ordinates had been changed but took Marc by complete surprise by asking if they could be changed yet again!

"You're not going to believe this but we have another rogue party!" Julie told him, sighing hard and clearly not joking.

This time it was RAI Radio in Italy. RAI were among a number of radio stations around Europe, which included Radio EINS in Berlin and Swiss Radio DRS in Zurich, who had reached deals with the local Sony Music affiliates to downlink the stereo mix and broadcast it live over their radio networks. Marc had been kept updated about these deals and had subsequently been issuing the co-ordinates to the confirmed radio partners. But the Sony Music HQ in New York had apparently not been consulted over a deal with RAI and objected to the terms the Rome office had independently made – except the station was arguing they would go ahead with the broadcast on the basis already agreed.

It was a lot to ask given it was now early Sunday evening and the co-ordinates had already been changed once at the last minute. To switch co-ordinates again now and succeed in properly updating everyone risked a lot of confusion. Even though he hated to say No, Marc couldn't help but feel compelled, for the first time, to decline a request, which he reasoned was asking for trouble. Julie could appreciate the situation and didn't force the issue, taking it in her stride like a real pro and resigning the matter as something the Rome office would have to settle. And both of them would just have to hope that they'd seen the last of these rogue parties otherwise they really would have a problem!

"Hey, come and see the satellite truck!" Marc said in higher spirits.

Marc led them onto the terrace and out through the side door to show them what the distribution process entailed. The first thing they saw was an unassuming, ordinary sized truck that could have been mistaken for a removal vehicle except for the 1.5 metre satellite dish fitted to its roof, which Marc explained could be electronically steered to face whichever direction any given satellite in space happened to be orbiting. The dish could transmit as well as receive data and vehicles like this were standard issue in the satellite business, to be found amidst war zones and music concerts alike. The truck's sliding side door was pulled back, exposing the compact array of small monitors, dials and switches that made up the "brain", all of it manned by a technician perched on a tiny stool. It was one heck of a toy!

Marc John could have checked into any fancy hotel in London but for some reason he chose a modest three star shack in Hampstead that wouldn't have been out of place on the travel itinerary of a budget backpacker. But it had a twenty four hour concierge, which was important since he knew he wouldn't be checking in until nearly 1am, and the bar was open too, which was handy for winding down after a long day and reviewing the evening's activities over a quick nightcap. He hadn't seen Bowie and wasn't sure if the star had actually shown up in the first place, but it could only be a matter of time before their paths crossed so it hadn't bothered him.

He was alone at the bar, apart from the concierge man at the reception desk who also doubled as a bartender whenever he saw Marc's glass close to empty. But he wouldn't have minded if some beautiful, mysterious woman joined him at the counter for a little flirtation and maybe more. That was his routine these days; to randomly meet girls in bars and have no serious intention of doing anything more than live for the moment. At that precise time he was actually dating three girls at once, but such philandering was little more than a disposable frivolity. Two of them had even sent him a good luck text message earlier that evening but he hadn't responded. Instead he applied a roguish, detached attitude toward his women that only a vintage James Bond could have exceeded. Ian Fleming may have approved but Napoleon's Josephine would have tutted. The Corsican man of history, for all his warring, at least knew the value of one true love.

The 9 pm and 11 pm tests had gone well enough, although they were limited to the cinemas that already had the complete spec of kit permanently installed, which was roughly only 20% of the sites. The other venues were being serviced with hired equipment that would arrive on the afternoon of the day of the event itself, but this was not a big concern. Provided everyone showed up on time and did their jobs, there was no reason to expect the rugged kit not to perform as required. Besides, booking all those services for two days instead of one would have made the economics of the event unviable in the first place.

The logistics for testing the two-way audio links for the Q&A were similarly awkward. With movies running throughout the day the mixer desks and microphones could only be brought in and tested in the morning, before the theatre doors opened for the first movie performance. The plan was therefore to test all the Q&A sites on the morning of the shows. But, as with the satellite kit, none of the Q&A technology was especially new and the key factor was again going be the technicians simply showing up on time and doing their jobs efficiently.

They hadn't been able to test the 5.1 audio either because the sites due to receive the multi-channel feed happened to be among those that were not permanently equipped with the complete spec of kit. This was leaving the crucial surround-sound innovation a little bit in the hands of chance but, as with those sites that couldn't be tested in any capacity whatsoever, there was just no choice. This was where digital cinema was in terms of its evolution and anyone pioneering the concept at that moment in time just had to fly by the seat of their pants to some degree.

He finally went to bed at around 3 am, having fitted in a few calls to Asia after learning that the satellite dish in Singapore had been blown off the theatre roof by a freak wind! The efficient ST Teleport were dealing with it, though, and even joked about putting a man up there to hold it down if necessary – which Marc was tempted to get in writing! He was so tired he fell asleep in his clothes with the light still on.

In the morning a new face had come on shift at the concierge desk and Marc had an important job for him.

"A courier is coming by to collect these," Marc said, handing over a stack of envelopes.

Inside the numerous envelopes were VIP tickets to see Bowie at Riverside, as well as tickets to watch the show at the Odeon West End theatre, which the courier would be hand delivering to the secretaries of the VIPs Marc wanted to make sure attended the event. This included numerous record label executives, trade journalists and not least the new CEO at Odeon.

Richard Segal, the charismatic, forward thinking Odeon chief, had departed suddenly over the summer shortly before the event was confirmed and it was a great pity that the man who had given him a tremendous start in the exhibition business would not be at the helm of Odeon for its first, truly spectacular success in the digital field. But while this was sad there was also the matter of making an immediate impression on the new boss and leaving whoever he or she was in no doubt that Marc John's contract at the end of the year should definitely be renewed!

Naturally, two VIP tickets to see Bowie live at Riverside made their way over to the new CEO at Odeon, a man named Ian Pluthero, whom Marc so far knew nothing about.

When he arrived at Riverside studios at 9 am Marc found that the classy Colin Black had laid on a full, buffet-style English breakfast for all the people working on the Bowie show, and he loaded up on scrambled eggs and sausage, not expecting another chance to eat until it was all over close to midnight.

At around 11 am CEST the Q&A line checks for the UK and Europe sites went ahead as planned and everything worked fine. The patchwork of freelance technicians were comfortable with the sequence and even over normal landlines the clarity was good. The satellite test to *all* the venues was next, scheduled for a full hour commencing at 3 pm.

After breakfast and non-stop until the early afternoon Marc had his cell phone glued to his ear making sure the satellite vendors and all the cinemas had received the revised satellite co-ordinates. He had taken to pacing along the embankment to make his calls, out by where the satellite trucks were parked, preferring to keep private some of the heat he was feeling.

"Marc, I'm not aware that we've cleared this David Bowie concert with the relevant local authorities," said Barry Keward, the number two at Odeon and the person Marc reported to on all his projects. "What can you tell me about that?"

Barry was referring to whether local authority approval had been obtained to permit the screening of material that hadn't been classified by the British Board of Film Classification, the censorship agency that certified movies shown in UK cinemas as being suitable for audiences of various ages; i.e. PG, 12, 15, etc. The BBFC had told Marc that a live event appeared to exempt itself from being certified since no material actually existed that could be viewed in advance. Nevertheless Barry wanted to make sure that no power tripping regional watchdogs were going to raise any surprise objections before or after the event.

"I've spoken to several local authorities," Marc began answering, "and the feedback was the same as what the BBFC told me, so we're fine."

"Do we have letters confirming that?" Barry pressed.

Marc didn't have letters, he hadn't asked for any and amidst all the other demands and deadlines of the project it hadn't even been a concern.

"No," he answered sheepishly.

"Well, we'll just have to hope that nobody tries to call the show off because we don't have written approval to exhibit an unrated concert to the public," Barry blasted, "and furthermore that we don't get fined afterwards!"

Marc rolled his eyeballs. He respected and liked Barry; the old Odeon stalwart had taught him a lot about how the cinema business worked and how to structure a deal, but sometimes he felt his immediate boss at Odeon wagged his finger far too sternly at him, perhaps because at thirty two Marc was still relatively young and probably looked upon as lacking a fully rounded acumen. As far as he was concerned Odeon had nothing to worry about, he knew what he was doing and felt he was further along in his professional apprenticeship than his mentor seemed to recognise.

When Marc came back onto the terrace deck through the side entrance from the embankment he met a sudden flurry of activity. A small crowd of people had emerged on the terrace from inside the studio building and they seemed to be huddled around someone. His eyes widened, the pulse quickened. It was *him*. Right there, unannounced, casual as could be, David Bowie had shown up for lunch! The singer took a table along with some of his inner sanctum but Marc didn't really notice who they were; he was zoomed in on the star and this blurred the periphery out of existence. His distance from Marc was less than two metres, almost close enough to see into the star's remarkable set of eyeballs, one brown and the other blue; famous in their own right for being so unique and mesmerising. The star's lips were moving; he was talking but not loudly and Marc couldn't hear the words. He wished he could; to hear that instantly recognisable voice and to know something of his mind. The presence of an icon was indeed doing something to him. Even the Voice was speechless! But he couldn't just stand there indefinitely. Luckily or unluckily, depending on how he was going to look upon it, his cell phone rang to break the spell.

It was the cinema manager in Rome. She was distressed that the satellite downlink engineer had turned up without any audio cables, thinking the cinema would have some, and as a result nobody knew how they were going to play the sound! Marc immediately headed back out onto the embankment to deal with the call, making sure that none of the behind-the-scene niggles were picked up by the Bowie table or anyone else for that matter. His role as the technical string puller had to work like a kind of magic, where nobody saw the technique and all its rough edges, just the marvellous, flawless end result.

"All he needs is a pair of phono cables," Marc told the panicking cinema manager, "get the engineer to go out and buy some, they're the most common audio cables you can buy and cost next to nothing, I can't believe what I'm hearing!"

Rome got busy as instructed and Marc was promised a call within the hour with an update. The Rome cinema, one of the UCI bunch, had been a particular trouble spot and Marc could have predicted a misadventure of some kind would arise. Originally the venue had been on Gerald Buckle's list of "fully equipped" digital sites but as the event neared Marc started getting emails from the cinema saying that the digital projector couldn't be used for some vague reason and then that the pre-existing satellite equipment could only be used if Sony rented it from UCI, despite this never being part of the original understanding.

But trusting UCI to reliably downlink the transmission even if the service *was* paid for fell into serious doubt when Marc learned that a small, independent satellite vendor – one whose bid for the Europe-wide downlink contract Marc had earlier rejected – was also the service contractor for UCI's satellite installations. Marc knew this company were sore at losing their bid and its managing director had even implied to Marc in an email that if Quantum Digital preferred another satellite company over his then his company wouldn't guarantee any of its satellite service obligations to UCI at all! Marc feared that a deliberate attempt at sabotage might be made at the UCI sites where this company was tasked with aligning the satellite dishes and programming the receivers and he told Buckle he would send in his own satellite people to make sure this didn't happen.

Marc did stop to wonder if he might be suffering from paranoia, but his fears were hardly eased when the satellite technician he sent to check UCI's pre-installed satellite kit at their Dublin cinema discovered that the dish on the cinema roof had been loosened from its brackets and moved out of alignment to W2! Incredibly Gerald Buckle wasn't bothered by it or convinced about the possibility of sabotage and scoffed at the dish movement as being weather induced. In fairness Marc couldn't rule this out but it didn't help his fraying nerves.

The UCI cinemas in Prague and Warsaw were less of a concern since they each had a team of genuinely dedicated people who Marc had a gut feeling could be trusted. But nevertheless he bluffed that extra technicians would be showing up anyway, just to make sure that even the slightest intention of skulduggery would be abandoned as futile. He felt justified having limited UCI's involvement at least, but still had to get through the event with several of their sites onboard and, as Rome was proving, the potential for disaster was still painfully apparent.

*Control emotion. Maintain focus,* the Voice computed as another incoming call sounded.

"The satellite truck hasn't arrived at the Munich cinema yet!" Florian Ritter called to tell him from Berlin. Florian was the event manager for the Cinestar chain in Germany where the show was booked to play on eight of their screens. Munich was particularly significant since it was one of the locations chosen to run the 5.1.

"It should have been there an hour ago!" Marc replied. "I'll check what's going on."

"It left late and it's stuck in traffic," Jorg Bruggen from T-Systems told him.

Jorg explained that the truck had a long distance to travel from some remote depot and the traffic hadn't been anticipated. It was too late to book another truck from someone else and there was no alternative to simply hoping it got there in time. Jorg wasn't any happier about it than Marc, who knew from dealing with the German in the past that he was a good, honest professional. Jorg had supervised the successful fibre relay from the T-Systems earth station in Usingen to Cinestar's Berlin cinema for the Melissa Etheridge broadcast and the two men had also met when Jorg made a special trip to the Cologne cinema on the night of the show, which had been a good piece of business development.

The 3 pm test was due in less than an hour but the start time for the show was still a solid six hours away, so the two men agreed to keep the sweat ducts at bay for now. But it put a crease in Marc John's forehead nonetheless and didn't bode well if T-Systems expected to grow the relationship. A score card was being kept on all the satellite vendors and the pass mark had to be high.

Elsewhere the satellite personnel were all running to schedule but this was actually little comfort. Having just two problem venues out of the sixty-eight that represented the UK and Europe portion of the global gig didn't qualify Marc for a congratulatory pat on the head for being ninety-eight percent on track. With every theatre sold out and a lot of hard Sony marketing dollars committed to each screening, the idea of cancelling just one show would be a microcosmic disaster with macrocosmic consequences. Marc was keeping a score card on himself too and it had to be higher than anyone else's! At least his affinity for James Bond came in handy, as he recalled an Ian Fleming line from *On Her Majesty's Secret Service* where the British secret service agent describes worry as "a dividend paid to disaster before it is due" – a philosophy Marc did his best to apply!

Bowie had finished his lunch and vanished somewhere inside the studio by the time Marc reappeared on the River Terrace after wrapping up his latest round of nerve bending telephone calls. The star had shown up for a rehearsal on stage with his band, scheduled for sometime between 3 pm and 4 pm, and the producer of the show from Blaze TV, Jim Parsons, told Marc he could use the feed for his mid-afternoon test if he wanted. This was perfect since it meant the technicians at the venues could fine tune their sound and picture using a broadcast of real performance rather than an empty, half-lit stage. But Marc didn't tell anyone what feed they were getting, wanting it to be a nice surprise instead.

As 3 pm closed in Marc was back to pacing anxiously along the embankment talking on his cell phone, trying to keep his grimaces and occasionally raised voice out of anyone's ear shot.

"If I cut you off I'll call you back," Marc told the UCI cinema manager in Rome, referring to the fact that his phone battery was fading. "Now what do you mean nobody knows how to connect the cables?"

It turned out that, between the satellite technician and the cinema staff, they had somehow managed to conjure up the required audio cables – except now they had trouble figuring out how to connect them to the cinema sound processor!

"How can your projectionist not know his own sound processor?" Marc asked, close to exasperation.

The situation was not helped by the manager's broken, incoherent English and the fact that nobody else at the cinema could speak or understand much English either!

"Just keep trying, try everything!" Marc insisted in-between the unintelligible staccato coming back at him down the line.

His phone battery was going to die at any moment and he had no choice but to run back into the production office to put it on charge. He slumped in his chair and couldn't resist closing his eyes for just a second or two. Every muscle in his body felt pinched by tiny clamps that were getting tighter and tighter, and not even another coffee stood much chance of jump starting him.

*Malfunctioning is not an option!* The Voice blared. *Override fatigue. Repeat. Override fatigue.*

But he was struggling and envied his cell phone, having its own little charger to juice it up in times of need. It seemed machines really did have it better! Then he detected a distinct noise coming through the walls from Studio 1 next door. It was the sound of music – and not just any music – it was Bowie and his band starting their rehearsal. It started to rouse him, lifting his hooded eyes and filling his tired body with renewed wattage. The star was playing and this he had to see!

Marc bolted up and darted out of the production office to make his way into the studio via the private entrance, eager to catch another privileged glimpse of the star. Inside the studio the floor space was barren except for a few crew members taping down cables and around them the Blaze TV cameras were zipping about, nailing their positions as they moved from one side of the stage to the other. The stage was beautifully lit with a gorgeous blue shimmer and at the front and centre there he was, David Bowie, singing a newly minted song called *New Killer Star* that was so far unheard to the outside world.

Decent beat, Marc thought, as his eyes zoomed in on the star. The first thing to strike him now was simply how *human* Bowie looked, that he was actually flesh and blood just like anyone else. He was wearing a tight green t-shirt that could have cost ten bucks and looked fitter and leaner than a lot of males more than half his age. His looks had fared well even with the weather of age, with distinct life lines chiselling his features in the way that can make a man look wise even if he isn't. He had heard Bowie was in the latter half of his fifties and, given the longevity of his career, it was quite something to see a man with that many miles on the clock still doing his thing with such verve. Marc felt practically embarrassed at feeling tired moments earlier, being a mere whippet in his early thirties!

If he could get an introduction it occurred to him that he should try getting a photograph as well. If he could he would be more than happy for Bowie to look every bit his age rather than his angular features be softened under somebody's air brush. Because, right then, Bowie was something of an inspiration and almost a reminder of what it meant to be a true artist – someone alive with that time-defying essence which can radiate throughout a lifetime no matter what the deceptions of the exterior. For all his years Bowie's light was still on. He was *beaming*.

Around Bowie was a six-piece band which looked fittingly cool and accomplished, although their illustrious careers and weight in gold to the singer was totally lost on the Aylesbury boy, who never followed music closely enough to appreciate the backing talent. Renowned figures such as Mike Garson on keyboards, Sterling Campbell on drums, Earl Slick and Gerry

Leonard on guitars, Gail Ann Dorsey on bass and Catherine Russell on percussion could have passed him in the corridor – and probably did – and he might easily have mistaken them for lowly production interns on the Blaze TV payroll! But this they were not and the troupe were in a good groove.

Marc could have stood there and watched the entire set but could only imagine how many calls he must have been missing on his gradually rejuvenating mobile phone. As Bowie and his band launched into the guitar strings and lyrics of the third track from *Reality*, an upbeat, punchy number titled *Never Get Old*, Marc took a final look at the amazing spectacle on stage and then slipped quietly out.

Before heading back to the production office he decided to pay a quick visit to the sound trucks to see how the sound supervisor, Tim Summerhayes, was getting on. Tim was sat comfortably in truck number one in a large leather recliner playing with dials and faders on a massive mixing console, and sat behind him lending his well schooled input was Bowie's long standing record producer, Tony Visconti. Both men were highly notable in their professions with Visconti particularly having an iconic status in his own right, having produced twelve Bowie albums as well as working with the likes of T-Rex and Thin Lizzy during a hallowed career that stretched back to the 1960s.

Marc hadn't met either man before and, as with Bowie's band members, wasn't familiar with their credits in the biz. Instead he said hello and shook their hands with the kind of understated, well-mannered ignorance that could just as easily have come across as being professional. Even though the sound mixing was the responsibility of Blaze TV and its audio partners at Sanctuary Sound and nothing for Quantum Digital to specifically oversee, Marc nonetheless wanted to find out what it entailed for the benefit of his ongoing technical edification.

Tim explained in his best layman's language that he was taking between fifty to sixty channels of audio from the production, which he called stems, and mixing them down to the six that would make up the 5.1 surround spectrum. It was a kind of distilling process where the stems were pruned into select branch ends and, once the six channels were mixed, he would prune them down further in order to create the two-channel stereo mix as well. The stereo would then get fed back to the second truck parked directly behind for a final quality check before both feeds were piped through that precarious cable run from the right side of the building to the satellite uplink trucks over on the left side.

It was an art form in itself and, in the case of a cinema broadcast, it was also something brand new to music sound mixers, given that the acoustics and dynamic range of a movie theatre represented a wholly different environment to mixing for CD or home DVD. To gauge how to reproduce six channels of music for the depth of space and the speaker arrangement of a movie theatre Tim had conducted a test a few weeks earlier in a London dubbing theatre using a six-channel mix he had worked on for the British female singer Dido. Nobody thought much about it right then but what they were doing had the potential to evolve into something highly specialised in audio engineering, where concert performances bound for cinemas would have their own totally unique mix compared to whatever is heard on a CD or DVD.

DTS had technicians in London, Munich, Paris and Zurich, where the 5.1 version was due to play during the first broadcast, with each of them telephoning David Pope with sporadic updates on how the 5.1 was sounding. David himself was personally supervising at Odeon West End and in turn was due to call Marc with feedback toward the end of the hour. It was likely each of these cinemas would need to rearrange the levels on their speakers to optimize the specially mixed 5.1, since virtually all cinema speaker systems were set at a pre-determined level for movies. Marc left the two men to get back to his cell phone to find out how they were getting on.

"I assume you know about Munich?" David Pope asked.

"I know but there's nothing I can do about it."

"Well, that's not our only problem ..." David continued.

Of all the places for the 5.1 software to throw a tantrum it was at Odeon West End, just a few miles down the road, where the DTS XD10 digital audio decoder was failing to perform.

"What's the problem with it?" Marc asked.

"We just don't know. We're working on it."

"Are they getting it in Paris and Zurich?" Marc asked.

"They're experiencing the occasional drop-out but we think we can overcome it."

That wasn't exactly what Marc wanted to hear. DTS had less than fifteen minutes to deal with it before the test expired and all he could do was let Pope get back to work and hope the concerns raised over bundling stereo with a DTS audio stream would not prove well founded after all.

More positively, there were messages from several cinemas confirming that the transmission was coming through loud and clear and what a wonderful surprise it was for the test broadcast to be the actual rehearsal. The euphoric voices almost put a smile on Marc's face, except for the couple of messages that were left from cinema technicians saying they were getting nothing at all. Not even a single pixel or the slightest crackle of sound. When Marc hastily telephoned these problem sites back to check what co-ordinates they were using it turned out the technicians had punched in the old digits instead of the new ones! There had apparently been a lack of communication between the cinema managers, who'd received the new co-ordinates, and the cinema staff in the projection booths who were responsible for programming them into the satellite receivers. What fun Marc was having!

Strangely, some of the other feedback from the cinemas reported that the aspect ratio of the picture was not widescreen 16 × 9 but square 4 × 3. This made no sense since Blaze were definitely shooting in widescreen, so Marc telephoned Kingston Inmedia to schedule another test feed to commence from 6 pm to run continuously until the actual start of the show, then alerted everyone to the extra fine tuning period. This would allow the satellite engineers to recheck the settings on their receivers as well as giving the DTS mob more breathing space to whip their technology into obedience. Fortunately he had built a contingency amount into the satellite budget for emergencies such as these, so at least there'd be no surprise bills landing on Julie's desk as a result.

When the extra test period started at 6 pm the UCI theatre in Rome had still not resolved its issues with the audio cables and the truck bound for Munich was still hugging the Autobahn. The 5.1 glitch at Odeon West End was still causing David Pope to scratch his head and grey hairs were sprouting from Marc's scalp as though it was their own special springtime! He was back pacing up and down along the embankment, probably getting enough exercise to last a month!

"It no work, it no good, nothing ..." the Italian accent despaired down the line from Rome.

The beleaguered UCI mob and satellite engineer were on the verge of giving up and cancelling the show altogether!

"You can't do that, you've got to keep trying!"

"But there is no more we can do!" the manager protested.

"Wait, I've got an idea!" Marc suddenly said in the throes of a brainwave. "Give me five minutes, don't cancel the show and stay by the phone!"

He ran back to the production office and grabbed his information sheet to find the one contact on it whose help could possibly save the situation, then quickly punched the number into his half charged, overworked cell phone.

"Laura, it's Marc, I need a favour!"

He had Laura Fumagalli on the line, the manager at the Arcadia multiplex in Milan, who spoke excellent English and whose cinema was among the most accomplished in Europe when it came to digital programming. The Bowie show was booked to play on two of Arcadia's screens, all the seats were sold out and Laura had handled everything with textbook efficiency. If anyone anywhere in Italy could come to his rescue it was her! Marc took the call out onto the terrace and explained his dilemma and that he needed one of her cinema technicians to get on the line to Rome and talk them through the process of wiring up the sound cables.

"Okay, Marc, we'll see what we can do," Laura said, taking down the number of the cinema and advising him to call back in fifteen minutes.

Meanwhile Jason Cooper from O$_2$ had arrived and was setting up his laptop on a desk in the production office in preparation to monitor and stream the text messages onto the UK screens. Jason got his program running without any problems and was able to upload a few test messages which he manually typed in. The caption generator in the production gallery did its job superimposing the text crawl along the bottom of the broadcast, which was now just a single camera shot of the empty stage, together with some pre-recorded audio, and this was outputted to the second uplink truck as the modified feed for the UK cinemas as intended.

Seeing Jason present Marc ran quickly out to the second uplink truck to check what the technician was seeing on his monitor, since this would match what audiences would see on the UK cinema screens. The text crawl looked good, similar to what a lot of music channels and reality TV shows ran along the bottom of the picture. He could feel relieved about that at least.

Fifteen minutes later:

"Laura, did you have any luck?"

"The projectionist there is not very technical," she began, "he must be a trainee."

What? A trainee on the night of a historic live broadcast to a packed house! Were they serious?

"Our people here are having trouble getting whoever this projectionist is to follow even the most simple instructions," Laura said.

"Unbelievable!" Marc uttered through flared tonsils. "Is there anything more you can do?"

"We're going to keep trying, we've got them playing around with different options, hopefully one of them will work ... "

All Marc could do was check back again in another fifteen minutes and continue to hope. In the meantime he could always take his mind off Rome by worrying about Munich instead. It was time to get Jorg Bruggen from T-Systems on the line again.

"The satellite truck just arrived," Jorg was relieved to report.

"That's good news."

"Yes, assuming he has time to lay the cables into the building!"

"Is he doing it?"

"I think he's getting himself a cup of coffee first!"

"That son of a bitch," Marc roared, "I'll rip his head off, put him to work!"

Next: David Pope at Odeon West End …

"Any luck?"

"We're baffled, Marc," David was embarrassed to say. "It's just not happening here at the moment. We think it might be something on the send end."

Marc went to find Ted and Andy, who were busy alternating between the two satellite uplink trucks, to tell them that the 5.1 problem in London was thought to be originating on the send end, which meant them, so what was the status?

"Well, those long cables are holding up and we're getting the mix from Tim in the truck without any problems," Andy started, "but we're having some difficulty with the encoding part to be honest, although it's just with the kit in the second truck for the UK feed, all the kit in the first truck sending out the Europe feed seems to be fine."

"So what's the problem?" Marc pressed. "Is it something to do with the $O_2$ text graphic maybe?"

"No, it's not that," Andy answered, "that's just an overlay on the picture, it's not interfering with any of our software."

"So is it the Tandberg encoder, your encoder, the cables, what?"

Andy and Ted simply didn't know and all they could do was check and recheck everything, constantly reboot their software and basically make the most of the time left to try rooting out the mysterious, dogged glitch. Marc gave them until 7.15 pm, which was fifteen minutes before the theatre doors were due to open to let people in, otherwise he would have to make a decision to go with stereo at Odeon West End instead. Nobody wanted this of course, not least DTS who had gone into marketing overdrive on how the London screening would be in glorious DTS 96 kilohertz-24–bit digital 5.1 surround-sound!

It was already just past the 6.30 pm mark and at Riverside itself the large bar area adjacent to the entrance to Studio 1 had started to fill up with the five hundred-strong VIP guests and Sony executives lucky enough to make up the live studio audience, along with a privileged handful of Bowie fans who had entered the text-to-win-tickets competition. The doors to Studio 1 were also due to open at 7.30 pm and the atmosphere was crackling nicely.

"Jorg, tell me he's ready!"

"He's almost there, he'll be ready," Jorg replied, referring of course to the Munich situation.

Almost wasn't good enough but they still had time. The satellite feed was going out non-stop now so there could be no excuses for everything not being fined tuned and perfect come showtime. Marc had issued instructions for cinemas and technical supervisors to contact him only if they were experiencing difficulties, rather than tie his line up with any other business. Naturally he didn't want to hear from any of them and so far he hadn't. The only person he was desperate to hear from was Laura in Milan about the Rome debacle.

"They're really in trouble, Marc," Laura winced telling him. "I don't know if they're going to make it ..."

"Just tell them to poke those goddamn cables into every hole they've got!" Marc countered. "And to make sure they've done nothing silly like leave a volume dial turned down somewhere!"

At 7.15 pm he was back with Ted and Andy at the second satellite truck, where they were still fiddling desperately with cables and menu settings on the encoders.

"It's going to be tight," Ted said. "I can't guarantee Odeon West End will make it. The European sites ought to be fine though."

Marc hadn't told them about Munich yet and it was an apt moment to get a call from Jorg in Germany.

"He's all set up and receiving the feed," Jorg started, "except he's only playing stereo because he didn't bring the right model of decoder box to play out the 5.1."

Marc laughed but not at all in a jolly way. He had nothing to say about it right then except that he'd talk to Jorg later. At least the show was running, he thought. This much was all he wanted to hear from Italy and the longer his cell phone stayed silent the tighter the ratchet in his belly was going to twist.

"We're in stereo in Munich," he told the DTS boys after hanging up with Jorg, "just don't ask me why right now!"

"What do you want to do about Odeon West End?" Ted asked. "I'd like to keep trying right up until the last possible second."

Marc agreed to hold the switch to stereo as late as possible, which meant 7.55 pm, five minutes before the performance was due to start. As it approached 7.30 pm the continuous satellite feed switched to a full screen shot of the *Reality* album cover and at 7.30 pm sharp the studio audience at Riverside started filing in, along with the doors opening at all the cinemas. The album cover shot seen on the UK screens also had a special cell number superimposed over it for people to send in text messages, and Jason started getting an SMS bombard even before the show went on air.

Meanwhile, at 7.50 pm, the audience in Rome were sat staring at the album cover on screen listening to some generic Italian music on the theatre's CD system while the cinema staff battled to extract the sound out of the satellite decoder in a dire race against the clock. No seat was empty and probably nobody in the audience could have imagined the despair going on behind the scenes. Instead they sipped their soft drinks and munched their popcorn eagerly awaiting what the local Sony Music marketers had hyped as an experience not to be missed!

"I must cancel!" The cinema manager in Rome called to tell Marc at 7.56 pm.

"You've still got four minutes for heaven's sake!" he thundered. "Use every last, goddamn second of it!"

And then Bowie and his band took to the stage to plug into their amps and take position as rapturous howls went up from the jam packed, supercharged live audience. The show's director, Julia Knowles, was getting ready in the production gallery to count down the switch from the album cover to the start of the performance and Marc had come back to the production office to watch it all on the widescreen plasma TV, which was also taking a feed of the broadcast. None of the cinemas or technical supervisors had called which meant all but Rome were tuned in and ready. Through the walls he could hear guitar strings and some percussion as the band started warming up and then, with literally seconds to go, in a manner that not even a Hollywood script writer could have contrived, came the last call he would take from Rome that night ...

"We did it, we have sound!" The euphoric Italian accent bellowed. "And now the show is starting!"

# 8

# ALL HIS POWERS

Up among the stars it was just another day at the office for W2. In the quiet ether of space the trusty satellite bounced the transmission beam back down to earth with a sophisticated ingenuity that would have made any of the old gods like Zeus, Vishnu or Yahweh run for the nearest 21st century science class! Round and round the shiny blue planet the wordless satellite went, knowing not day or night but only a permanently lit universe, like the wheel of eternity itself, transcending duality and language, yet intrinsic to each. With reliable irony here was a perfectly engineered symbolism that Man himself had made yet saw only the substance of. If these hi-tech deities were worried about how they were going to replace the gods of the past, whose metaphorical imagery was long overdue for a software upgrade, they needn't have worried. Their potential was vast.

Back on earth Marc was tempted to relax. Nobody had called to report any problems and he was even starting to enjoy the show. Before long the production office filled up with numerous faces from Sony, and everyone sat watching the show on the plasma TV with drinks brought in from the bar as a nice party atmosphere started to take over. Julian Stockton was there too. Julie was somewhere in the audience on the studio floor itself while Robert Young had wanted to experience the show at a cinema and was watching it at Odeon West End.

The show had switched to stereo at Odeon West End after the DTS team were unable to solve the problem in time, although efforts continued even after the show had started to see if they could switch to 5.1 at some point during the performance. It was hardly an ideal outcome but at least they were running 5.1 in two out of the four theatres and the event now genuinely marked the first time in the world that digital 5.1 audio had been broadcast live to cinemas. The number was almost incidental. Besides, in London and Munich, as well as everywhere else where the 5.1 was not fed, the stereo was played through the surround speakers to tremendous effect.

As Bowie launched into his fourth song, *The Loneliest Guy*, Marc decided to take a peek at the show from inside Studio 1 itself, given that his AAA pass meant he could access the jamming studio floor at his leisure. How intimate it felt, like something that could have been laid on in a Manhattan loft apartment for people on the block to casually pop in and enjoy over a glass of Chardonnay.

The new chief at Odeon, Ian Pluthero, was somewhere in the bopping crowd too, but having not met the man yet Marc wouldn't have recognised him anyway. He just hoped Pluthero hadn't missed out on coming for whatever reason and that he was being suitably wowed by what his industrious contractor was delivering.

Marc kept to the back of the studio, standing off from the huddled throb of swaying bodies, since he wasn't really there to be part of the audience. Before heading back to the production office he just wanted to see if he could spot any celebrities. Rumours were that some big names were planning to come and support Bowie and his eyes raked over the studio looking for any privileged vantage points that may have been reserved for special guests.

It occurred to him to glance up at the narrow walkway at the top of the iron steps that ascended from the studio floor to the production and sound galleries, and sure enough Marc spotted a star. It was Bob Geldof, the former lead singer of the 1970s Brit group the Boomtown Rats, but more famously known as the man behind the Band Aid and Live Aid charity projects.

Geldof was all by himself and looked very relaxed, moving his head to the music and lightly tapping his foot. Perhaps he was getting the idea to do a similar cinema gig for a future Live Aid reunion, Marc imagined. He licked his lips at the thought of it,

wondering if he should try cornering Sir Bob to actually pitch
the idea! He was totally untroubled by any sense of guilt over
such an opportunistic urge. After all, if Geldof was game for it
how guilty could he feel about pocketing a sweet fee if it meant a
few million dispossessed Africans would have an easier life for a
few months as a result? By now he was not beyond succumbing
to that most dangerous of profit validations; where men swell
their pockets in the name of aid, convinced that the interest
served is collective when really it is personal. And if he was
honest he would not even be able to claim that he was adding his
light, for in truth he would be *trading* it.

Pitching Geldof would have to wait. As Bowie breezed
through his performance it was getting close to the Q&A
segment, which the popular British TV presenter Jonathan Ross
was set to host, and Marc wasn't going to feel home and dry
until this, the most technically complex part of the event, was in
the bag. He looked around the studio once more to make sure
there was nobody else there he should try pitching and then
slipped out to head back to the production office.

As Bowie wrapped up the album set with the sombre, jazz
inspired *Bring me the Disco King* the affable Jonathan Ross
prepared to appear on stage to moderate the Q&A session. Ross
had a talk show on BBC1 that Bowie was due to appear on later
that week and he was also a big Bowie fan, which made him the
ideal choice to host the segment. As thunderous applause rained
down at the close of the song the always dapper Ross glided
onto the stage to shake the singer's hand, and a couple of stools
were popped on stage by a pair of nimble crew hands for them
to sit on while the band sank into the background for a breather.

Meanwhile local radio DJs, who had been recruited by the
regional Sony offices, were ready with microphones at each of
the Q&A venues to ask pre-selected audience members to stand
up and put their question to Bowie. Weeks earlier it had been
announced on Bowie's website that a shortlist of people would
get to ask questions and hundreds were subsequently submitted.
By September 4th the best eight questions had been picked and
the winners contacted via email to confirm they would definitely
be attending the show. Jonathan Ross had been given the pre-

arranged order in which the questions would be asked and would cue each local host when it was their turn to fire away.

Fans from eight major cities were now going to get their chance to talk directly with their idol and as Ross and Bowie settled down for the two-way audio links everyone in Studio 1 as well as in the production office fell quiet in an excited hush of anticipation. The first question was due to come from a girl called Josefine in Berlin, watching from the Cinestar theatre at 4 Potsdamme Strasse. Marc held his breath ...

"Hello Berlin, are you there?" Ross asked.

There was no answer.

"Berlin? Are you hearing us?"

The two-way audio was set up so that everyone in Studio 1 could hear the questions as well as all the cinemas, and unless Josefine spoke up soon everyone was going to hear loudly and clearly that Berlin had a problem!

"Berlin?" Ross tried again, now seemingly in vain.

The experienced TV presenter shifted uncomfortably on his stool while Bowie looked a little perplexed as well. It was a heart stopper. Marc silently cursed, trying not to catch eyes with anyone else in the production office. The sense of bewilderment was palpable but Jonathan Ross was experienced enough to deal with it and, without looking too ruffled, put the question to Bowie on Josefine's behalf, which was: "I own a lovely Great Dane named Jones, what happened to your dog Etzel?"

Marc didn't hear what happened to Etzel because his face was buried in his hands and his head was spinning. What the hell had happened? He had no idea and this was only the first question!

*Override personal meltdown! Repeat override personal meltdown!* The monotone Voice blared so anxiously that it probably needed to heed its own advice!

Marc quickly pulled himself together and dragged his eyes back up to the plasma TV, knowing that losing just one of the eight questions would not be such a disaster. The next question was due from a fan called Eugenia who was at the MK2 Bibliothèque multiplex at 128 Avenue de France in Paris ...

"Okay, over to Paris," Ross continued, "Paris, are you there?"

The phone line crackled into life and a sweet sounding French voice was soon audible, raising hope that Berlin was indeed an isolated blip.

"Yes, this is Paris. Yes, this is Paris ..."

But there was something odd about the connection, there seemed to be an *echo* down the line! Eugenia probably couldn't tell and launched into her question regardless, which was: "How does literature influence your writing and do you ever feel like singing about what you've read?"

Marc's ashen face sunk back into his sweating palms because not only was there a terrible echo but there was also a loud, screeching noise on the line that made the question barely decipherable in the first place! It couldn't have sounded too pleasant in Bowie's earpiece either and even the usually unflappable Jonathan Ross couldn't help but grimace. Heck, even Berlin sounded better!

Somehow Bowie managed a laudable comeback to the question and Jonathan Ross moved it along in good enough spirits to keep it from being a total disaster just yet. But Marc didn't know if he could take any more. Even if the next six questions ran perfectly the two faults were going to haunt him forever. His perfect technical record from that moment was gone and the golden boy was in danger of being bronze beneath the veneer!

The next question came from Mads at the Empire Bio theatre at 29 Guldbergsgade in Copenhagen and mercifully there were no problems. Amsterdam was next and a girl called Miriam smoothly came on the line from the famous Dutch concert arena the Melkveg; although by now Marc wasn't properly registering what the questions were, only that they were audible in the first place. It was four down with four to go but with a "success" rate of 50–50 it was hardly the sort of odds he would have enjoyed knowing in advance.

But next up was Odeon West End in London, just a few miles down the road. Surely his own Odeon backyard was the one place he could count on. Jonathan Ross called on a fan named Richard to speak up from Odeon West End – but the line was silent. And it stayed silent! London was dead. That was it, time to disappear. Marc didn't want to stick around to see what happened with the three remaining cities on the Q&A list – Oslo, Milan and Stockholm – and headed for the exit. It could now be concluded that the Q&A session was a certified disaster no matter how it finished off.

Further along the corridor outside the production office was a door leading out onto the River Terrace, and as Marc walked dejectedly onto the deck and over to the railing facing the Thames he kept thinking about what a big star David Bowie was and how he had just made him look a fool. It wouldn't even be much consolation to know that the last three questions all went off without a problem. There were going to be disappointed fans where the Q&A had failed and *all* the cinemas, plus everyone at Riverside, had been exposed to the failings. This was hardly going to do much good for the concept. And the new Odeon chief had witnessed it all too! How quickly and dramatically a perfect night, a dream night, had given way to the stuff of nightmares. He felt wretched.

Moments later Bowie and his troupe could be heard launching into the first of the seven encore songs, *Fantastic Voyage,* but Marc couldn't face going back inside just yet. He was alone on the terrace and needed the space. Another exit door was heard to open, this time from Studio 1 itself, and Marc turned to see Jonathan Ross come striding out onto the deck fresh from his stint and obviously somewhat relieved.

"Can you believe that Q&A?" Ross said to Marc with a disappointed shake of the head.

Marc didn't expect that Jonathan Ross knew who he was or what impact a comment like that might have and he couldn't even muster a reply. Instead he just let the TV star walk on by to re-enter the building via another entrance, a shortcut for Ross to get to his dressing room on the other side of the building. Marc turned back to lean forlornly over the railing, and wouldn't have minded if a vacationing Loch Ness monster leapt out of the abyss to gobble him up as a late night snack!

He wouldn't have much time to lick his wounds. As soon as the gig was over some after-show hobnobbing was expected to spill out onto the terrace and he would have to engage in the chit chat and no doubt explain a few things to a number of enquiring minds. What happened to those hi-tech gods, he wondered, were they going to prove as inconsistent as the temperamental divinities of the past? And how desperately he wished to truly be in love right at that moment, to have a woman's comforting arms to retreat into and feel that things were not so bad after all.

"Congratulations!" Robert Young called to say immediately after the final credits on the show had rolled.

"Are you kidding?" Marc replied forlornly.

"What do you mean? We've got a hit on our hands!" Robert raved.

"What about the problems with the Q&A," Marc countered, "didn't that ruin everything?"

"Hell, no!" Robert insisted. "That didn't really bother anyone and if anything it proved the show was live. We did it!"

"But I still screwed up, Robert," Marc said. "Bob Geldof was here too, I'd hate to think it put him off doing a cinema gig!"

"Have a drink!" Robert told him. "I'll call you tomorrow after the second broadcast."

As the terrace started filling up with Sony people and a few VIPs Marc had almost forgotten that he had to go through the whole thing again with Singapore, Hong Kong, Japan and Australia at noon BST the very next day. Where was he going to get the strength?

*Debug yourself! Are you a machine or a mouse?* The tinny Voice blasted. *Think BT. Think Sony Business Europe. Think UCI ...*

Yes, of course, he had to think about his rivals. Those bastards were probably falling over in glee that he'd screwed up, and no doubt they couldn't wait for him to pack up and bow out of the game altogether, leaving all the turf he'd ploughed for them to harvest. No way! He still had tomorrow to get it right, as well as the third broadcast on the following Monday. All was not lost and Marc John stiffened his back to finish out the night.

Before the night was over there was a quick, private review in the "green room", the plush waiting area where celebrities are parked prior to coming out to perform, where Marc explained to Julie, Julian Stockton and a few of the Blaze team that the

Q&A problems were confounding, considering that everything had worked perfectly during the rehearsal earlier in the day. Nevertheless, the feedback overall was positive and nobody was downbeat. Bowie was happy with everything and it turned out that even *he* had made a mistake, apparently forgetting the words to *Modern Love* during the encore.

"We're only human after all," Julie remarked.

*Speak for yourself!* The Voice commented defiantly.

The next day was less frenetic, with the live Q&A segment being filmed by just two or three stationary cameras against a sparsely dressed backdrop, after the pre-recorded show was broadcast instead of a second live performance. The VHI presenter Paul King had taken over the Q&A moderation from Jonathan Ross, who had only been available for the first session.

The sequence was for the four Greater Union-Hoyts theatres in Australia – two in Sydney and two in Melbourne – to go first with a question each, which the Australian television personality Richard Wilkins was in position to host from the George Street cinema in Sydney, followed by the Tokyo venue getting two questions with Singapore and Hong Kong finishing it off with a question apiece.

Marc was back in the production office glued to the plasma TV, along with Julian Stockton and some other Sony people, as the switch from the tape to the live Q&A feed took place. Marc hadn't been able to look Stockton in the eye the night before and could only pray he wasn't in for a similar furnace of embarrassment.

The first question came in beautifully, sounding as crystal clear all the way from Down Under as a call from around the corner. And so did the second, third and fourth calls that rounded up the Q&A portion from Oz. This was more like it. Marc was slowly remembering how to smile again and out of the corner of his eye he could see Julian Stockton punching the air in triumph that they were getting the tricky process right this time.

The next call from the SME Nogizaka Building in Tokyo produced two, further flawless connections and now Marc's heart was racing not because he was afraid of failing but because they were now so very near to getting to the last call without experiencing even the slightest hitch. This time Kevin Duff, the call switcher at Riverside, had instructions not to hang about if there were any delays at the venue and to jump right to the next city as smoothly as possible if it sounded like a line was in trouble.

But Kevin may have been just a little too trigger happy with the advice, as the host on the next line from the Cathay Leisure Centre in Singapore seemed to take perhaps just two or three seconds too long to respond when Paul King greeted the cinema and asked if they could hear him. Kevin cut them off rather than risk any embarrassing silences and the competent Paul King was equal to the task of seamlessly moving along to the next and last question from the Hong Kong Convention and Exhibition Centre, which fortunately rounded the segment off without any problems of its own. It was a six out of seven success rate and after what happened the night before it had to be considered a jolly good result.

"Mister John, this Singapore here, what happen?" A flustered oriental voice wailed to Marc down his cell phone moments later.

It turned out the line from Singapore would have been fine and that the host was merely summoning his best powers of English before responding to Paul King's welcome. The theatre wanted to get patched back onto the call so that the eager and apparently upset fan could go ahead and ask her question. But by then Paul King had wrapped it up and Bowie was off camera with Blaze already switched back to the tape for the encore numbers.

It was a shame for Singapore but the packed theatre had at least loved every note of the performance, Marc reassured himself, and they had still got to see Bowie answering live questions from the other locations. He could have rollicked Kevin Duff for being too hasty on the call switcher but he hadn't got around to handing out the requisite verbal lashings to those shifty freelance mixers on the continent yet, so decided to save his finger wagging for those who deserved it most. Besides, Julian Stockton had already pulled plenty of great feedback off the web to restore Marc John's faith in the whole, fragile process, which he had printed out at home and brought in to pass around.

"David Bowie's plan to broadcast a gig live to cinemas around the world worked brilliantly!" Raved William Gallagher, a journalist who had watched the show at Odeon Birmingham and reviewed it for the BBC website. "The show was filmed extremely well to bring a sense both of being close to the action and remaining part of what seemed a very intimate London stage. The second half came more alive as Jonathan Ross hosted a question and answer set with Bowie, which suffered enough technical problems to be fun."

Fun? Hardly, Marc thought.

"At the little cosy Empire cinema in central Copenhagen I arrived with my sister, her boyfriend and two other friends," wrote Jesper Olsen in Denmark, "the new album sounded great and the show had such a great feeling of intimacy. The band was great, especially Gail Ann Dorsey, who I have a huge crush on. Magisk!"

"I saw the show at the Draken in Stockholm," wrote Lars Björck in Sweden, "the show was awesome, the new songs were great. There were sound problems during the Q&A section but who really cares about that?"

What a lift it was reading that people weren't as disappointed with the Q&A shambles as Marc imagined they would be. Maybe he had gotten away with it after all. Was Geldof reading any of this?

"Was this broadcast to any cinemas in the USA? Shame if it was as I wasn't aware of this gig!" Antje Stobbe in the US posted.

"Dearest Antje, you'll still have the chance to see this event in America next week," a friendly Belgian named Merlijn Marsman posted in reply, "so look out for tickets!"

That's nice, Marc thought, smiling at how the cordially disposed Internet had made the passage of information between two, distant strangers so conveniently effortless.

"We were at the MK2 cinema in Paris with nearly 2,500 Bowie fans," wrote Jacques in France, "the broadcasting through satellite was great, the sound was wonderful. David Bowie has the silhouette of a 25–year-old man, his voice is perfect, and the energy of the band is amazing."

"I went to the concert with my wife and daughter, it was a great show," said Paul Komender from Warsaw, "the personal contact with the audience in the theatre was great."

"Bowie looked great on the big screen and the picture was crystal clear," wrote James Tully in the UK, "it was a bargain as well. I probably could have paid about £50 to see an 'actual' concert and still be sat right at the back looking at a video screen. More events like this please!"

*Marc will do his best, James.* The Voice assured.

All this was great but what about Rome, Marc desperately wondered? He scoured the web looking for someone who had been at that wretched UCI cinema hoping to find, after all the drama and near tragedy, that the show had finally proved a success as far as the audience were concerned.

"I was in Rome in the UCI-CINEMAS MARCONI ... " an Italian named Walter Bianco was eventually found to have posted, "together with other Italian Bowie fans from the online fan club Velvet Goldmine, and we witnessed a great show. Long live Bowie!"

Sleep would come a little easier now and Marc could set his sights on the third and final leg of the cinema tour in America, knowing if it could match the near perfection of the second transmission that the early Q&A hiccups would be lost in the overall acclaim, his reputation would remain virtually unblemished and his position in the industry would remain unequalled. The likes of BT, Sony Business and anyone else wanting a piece of his action could keep on grinning if they thought the foul ups from Monday were going to trip him up. He'd show them!

"You'll have the tapes by the end of the day," Blaze producer Jim Parsons promised.

Jim was referring to the three dubs Marc needed for Canada, Brazil and New York, which had to be in different picture ratios as per the requirements established on his conference calls with the Canadian and Brazilian cinema partners. It was an urgent job since the tapes had to get sent out with enough

time ahead of the following Monday for all the theatres to do a
quality check.

Meanwhile Julie asked if there was any chance that the band
and some Sony Music executives could have tickets to the
Manhattan screening, since New York was Sony Music's HQ
and it would be a great opportunity to showcase the concept to a
lot more of their marketing directors. Marc didn't have a
problem with the request. After all, he wanted Sony Music to
supply regular live programming as much as anyone else and if
the screening could reinforce the sales job on them then so much
the better! One thing he always remembered from being a real
estate agent in Manhattan all those years earlier was that the
selling doesn't stop when the client buys, the selling keeps on
going because a client is not a client once but a client for life.

"Anything for you, Julie," Marc told her, throwing in some
charm for good measure.

Bowie's album producer Tony Visconti was also keen to
attend the Manhattan show, and wanted to gain access to the
theatre in advance to check the EQ system and tweak the sound
levels. Marc said this shouldn't be a problem either and
arranged to rendezvous with Visconti in the Manhattan theatre
lobby at a predetermined time on the afternoon of the show, and
to stay in touch via their cell phones if the timing had to change
for any reason.

"Feeling better?" Robert Young called him on the Tuesday
afternoon to ask.

"Much better thank you."

"I was worried about you. I thought you were going to jump
in the Thames!"

"The thought had crossed my mind, but the reviews are
cheering me up."

After a little more mutual, congratulatory talk Robert went
on to say that he and Julie wouldn't be back in the States the
following week for the show on Monday and that Marc was
more than welcome to stay at their penthouse apartment in
Manhattan's exclusive Sutton Place neighbourhood. It was very
generous and since Marc had yet to book a hotel he was happy
to take him up on the offer. It reflected how well the trio had

bonded, personally as much as professionally, and increasingly Marc could see himself taking up Robert's other offer of entering into a business partnership.

Robert was the closest thing Marc had seen to himself in terms of having a real entrepreneurial appetite for digital cinema – and fortunately he wasn't a rival! Combining their complimentary skills seemed more and more like the right thing to do and Marc finally decided it would be less a case of power shared and more that of power doubled. When it was all over he planned to sit down with his Irish friend to talk about how rosy their future could be.

By the end of Tuesday Blaze hadn't managed to run off the tape dubs as promised and the late afternoon deadline for getting them out on an overnight courier passed, much to Marc's frustration. He had to tell Famous Players in Canada and Teleimage in Brazil that they'd arrive by Thursday instead, which was still enough time for their satellite uplink and picture tests, but what started to worry Marc now was that, with Blaze's contribution to the project more or less finished, they had somewhat of a blasé attitude toward taking care of the loose ends. When Wednesday came and went without the tapes appearing Marc even wondered if BT's Gary Condon or SBE's Kevin Wakeford were quietly moonlighting at Blaze and deliberately sidelining the work to frustrate the hell out of their arch-rival!

"Tell Gary and Kevin to hurry it up, Jim!" Marc boomed down the telephone.

"What?" Jim blanked.

"Private joke, forget it. But seriously it's urgent I get those tapes."

The earliest that Canada and Brazil would get the tapes now would be Friday, the day Marc was scheduled to fly out of the UK himself. If he didn't get the tapes by mid-Thursday there was going to be more than a slight problem. In the midst of all this he hadn't managed to contact and invite any US press to the Manhattan screening. Instead he had to rely on the joint press release Quantum Digital had issued with DTS, which DTS had taken responsibility for circulating.

Somewhere between aspirin packets Marc did manage to find
time for the international money transfer that Regal cinemas in
the US had demanded as the method of payment for the hire of
their theatre, as well as making himself available for a couple of
important journalists who were thirsting for some comments on
the Bowie gig. Among them was a reporter named Paul Sexton,
who wanted to do a big article on the cinema show in the music
trade publication *Billboard*.

Getting a mention in a global trade bible like *Billboard* was
just the kind of publicity Mr Quantum Digital craved and from
his Odeon office on the Thursday morning, whilst waiting for
the tapes to arrive from Blaze, Marc excitedly told Sexton all
about the digital revolution and Quantum's part in everything.
And much to his delight, in an article titled "Bowie Simulcasts
Reality", Sexton even quoted him by name.

Marc was doubly pleased because the article also referred to
him in both his capacity as Head of Digital Cinema for Odeon
as well as the Managing Director of Quantum Digital. His
principal paymasters couldn't be forgotten in all the hype, of
course, and it was good to get their name in print. Building
Odeon's profile in the digital era had to remain as much a focus
as anything if he was to keep his bread and butter pay cheques.
Indeed, he was twitching for a sit down with the new chief, Ian
Pluthero, who surely must have come away from Riverside
buzzing like the rest of them.

And sure enough that week Marc got a call from Pluthero's
secretary saying that the boss wanted a meeting to discuss all
things digital. It would have to wait until he got back from the
States, of course, but after that he was free anytime and a couple
of tentative dates were pencilled in for the secretary to check
with Pluthero.

In the meantime, where were those goddamn tapes? The slack
attitude was completely out of character with how marvellously
Blaze had operated when producing the show. Matters weren't
helped when Marc called Federal Express to find out what their
latest cut-off time was for pick-ups only to be told that the cut-
off point for an express delivery to South America had already
passed – that two days was the quickest shipment time and this

excluded weekends! With it being Thursday already a package to Sao Paolo therefore wouldn't stand a chance of getting there until Monday, the day of the show!

Marc tracked down Jim Parsons and found that the dubs had been done except for some reason they hadn't left the dubbing suite. Marc took drastic measures and had a local motorcycle courier collect the Brazil copy and whisk it over to Kingston InMedia where the new plan was to beam it out via satellite for Jerome Merle to downlink at Teleimage's satellite earth station instead of waiting until Monday for the tape to arrive, which would have meant virtually no time for testing. Fed-Ex were at least able to guarantee next day delivery for Canada and Dave MacGregor's secretary at the Sony Music offices in London was gracious enough to take care of it while Marc took care of Brazil.

The third tape for Manhattan he could collect personally from the edit suite in London's Soho district en route to Heathrow rather than trust Royal Mail's special delivery service, just in case, of course. He still hadn't packed for his flight and suddenly what was expected to be a plain sailing process after Tuesday's virtually perfect second broadcast and glowing feedback was now descending into the kind of chaos he thought he'd seen the back of.

"Is everything okay for Monday?" Robert checked on a routine call.

Marc could have done with a sense of humour but for now he had to put up with a resurgent frown. He explained the situation and that he was dealing with it. The final broadcast was also the most important as far as Marc was concerned. Not only would it complete the event's reach across the planet but it was all happening from New York, his former home and the place where he became a man. Ending the history-making project in Manhattan couldn't have made it more special and he was going to bring all his powers into play to make sure it was perfect.

Luckily his contingency budget for satellite services just about covered the unanticipated transmission he had to book to get the show over to Brazil but any extra spending from that point on was going to exceed his cost forecasts, something he promised wouldn't happen. But, provided Canada got their tape promptly the following morning, Marc wasn't going to feel like he was living too dangerously just yet.

Early in the afternoon on Friday September 12th Marc took the Aylesbury-to-Marylebone train as usual and then hopped in a taxi to take him to Heathrow, making a quick stop in Soho along the way to grab the tape for New York. Shortly before arriving at Heathrow he got a call from Jerome in Sao Paolo confirming that they'd successfully downlinked the show and had it stored on their drives, except there was one little problem. Jerome had checked the show and found that the Q&A section, hosted by Jonathan Ross, hadn't been edited out. Blaze were supposed to have done this so that the footage was perfectly cued to fade out at the end of the album performance and then fade in again for the encore set, with the break in-between indicating where the switchover to the live Q&A had to be made. Without the original Q&A being edited out it was going to be extremely difficult for all three countries to know precisely where to stop the show and precisely where to start it again.

"We'll just have to pay very close attention to the frame counter and cue up three times," Marc said.

But it was more fraught and fiddly than it needed to be and he started to scratch his head for possible alternatives. Sure, they could all note the exact frame on which to stop the show after the album set and then note the exact frame on which to restart after the new Q&A but there was considerably more room for error now given that they would have to cue their tapes three times instead of just once at the start. And if any of the three countries were too many seconds out on the first or second cues it was possible they could miss the start of the Q&A and perhaps even a question or two!

*Virus-free show essential,* the Voice reminded. *Take all necessary precautions against crash.*

If he was going to come up with another plan it would have to take into account that his contingency budget was now fully exhausted. Still, he had the six-hour plane ride to think it over and probably a night of restless sleep to think it over some more, so what the hell was he worrying about? Before boarding the plane he heard from Canada that they'd received the tape and were checking it out that afternoon, so at least both countries had the material, and with the New York tape in his personal possession the situation could have been far worse.

That evening back in the UK David Bowie made his appearance on the BBC1 chat show *Friday Night with Jonathan Ross* but Marc wouldn't have seen it, of course, since by then he was knocking back a few of the beers chilling in the fridge of Robert and Julie's swanky penthouse apartment. In a lively interview Bowie was very upbeat about the cinema gig, which Ross spent a decent amount of time going into, remarking how it was a world first event and that cinemas had never played live 5.1 sound before either. Unfortunately Ross wasn't shy about highlighting the technical troubles they'd suffered either and if Marc had caught the show he would not have been too amused with how the chatty interviewer seemed to be judging the success of the event on the merits of the Q&A section alone!

The TV coverage planned in the US for the album launch included an interview on the CBS news magazine show *60 Minutes*, an interview and three-song set on *The Today Show* on NBC, as well as slots on the country's two leading late night talk shows, *The Late Show with David Letterman* and *The Tonight Show with Jay Leno*. Media exposure in America didn't get any bigger than all of this, and if the gig got mentioned as it had done during the Ross interview it would give digital cinema precisely the kind of promotional boost that Marc was hoping for, assuming there were no gaffes of course ...

Marc certainly found Robert and Julie's penthouse to his liking. Located on 53rd near the East River, it had a massive terrace with a spectacular view of the Manhattan skyline. Inside, hanging on the walls in the hallways, Marc couldn't help noticing numerous gold discs that had been awarded to Julie by Sony Music for her outstanding contribution to album sales figures over the years.

He was also fascinated by an assortment of expensively framed photographs hanging on the living room wall, where Julie and Robert were pictured with a number of public luminaries including Hillary Clinton and, in one particularly intriguing pose, Robert was stood smiling shoulder to shoulder with Gerry Adams, the Irish political revolutionary and leader of Sinn Fein – the movement that had been waging a campaign since 1905 to throw off the shackles of British imperial rule in Ireland. Sinn Fein and the notorious Irish Republican Army were often construed as being one and the same and, whatever the case, Adams was not a man to be messed with. Perhaps Robert was a man to treat carefully too, Marc suddenly thought, taking great care to rest the picture back where he found it!

By the time a yellow cab from JFK airport had got him into the city it was already the early evening and, much as he wanted to walk around and soak up the atmosphere of the city, what he really needed was an early night. He had arranged a test at the Regal theatre at 8 am the following morning, which meant it was more of a working weekend than time off. But if he was lucky he would have Sunday free to check out some old neighbourhoods, wander into Central Park and maybe even have a look in the Barnes & Noble bookstore on West 83rd Street.

At 8 am sharp the next morning Marc arrived at Regal's Union Square multiplex at 800 Broadway, near 14th Street, to rendezvous with Carl Greenburg and Carl Campbell, the technicians assigned by DTS to oversee the 5.1 side of the show. The two Carls, along with Jurgan Zahn, the regional technical services manager for Regal, were already in the foyer when Marc arrived. After the perfunctory hand shaking and chit-chat they proceeded up to the projection booth, which was on the top floor of the tall, multi-storey theatre complex. Thankfully there was a service elevator and also a series of public escalators connecting each of the three floors, so hauling the heavy kit wasn't a nightmare.

"I've got the DTS 5.1 media player with me," Carl Greenburg said referring to the big, black flight case he was pushing on a wheel mount, "is the tape player on the way or what?"

"I thought you were bringing the tape player," Marc replied.

"No, I thought *you* were bringing it!" Carl shot back.

But Marc had never planned to bring along the required digital Betacam tape player deck. The arrangement he was sure he had made with DTS was that he'd supply the tape and DTS would handle the rest, to include the 5.1 decoder *and* the tape player. This was not what the two Carls had been told and without the all-important tape player there could be no test of the sound and picture. In fact, if they couldn't come up with a tape deck by Monday the show itself would be in jeopardy!

"So you're telling me we need to get hold of a deck at the weekend of all times?" Greenburg asked, letting his mouth gape at the end of it.

"It looks like it," Marc answered, no happier about the mix up.

"And let me guess," Greenburg went on, stabbing a finger at the digital cassette tucked under Marc's arm, "you had to go and bring a PAL version right, not NTSC?"

"Well, yeah, that's right, it's PAL."

"Whadda ya know, the kid wants miracles!" Greenburg boomed, laughing and throwing his hands up. "Getting hold of a deck at the weekend is gonna be tough enough, let me tell ya, but getting hold of a PAL deck when most of the players over here are NTSC is really pushing it!"

Greenburg, doing all the talking, was clearly the more senior of the two Carls. He was in his late forties and had the kind of wise cracking, old school persona distinctive to a lot of native New Yorkers. Carl Campbell, in contrast, was probably not out of his twenties yet and had the kind of unassuming, studious disposition that gave the pair a kind of mentor-apprentice equipoise which the latter seemed happy to defer to.

"Okay, there's been a mix up," Marc countered, keeping calm. "All we can do now is deal with it. Do you know anyone who can fix us up?"

"I know a guy in New Jersey who's probably the only person on the entire east coast who can save this," Greenburg answered. "If he picks up the phone you might just be in luck ..."

By then they had reached the top floor, exited the service elevator and were heading along a long, narrow corridor toward the entrance to the projection backrooms, led by the chuckling Jurgan Zahn, who was clearly amused by the antics.

"I better get you guys some coffee!" said the Regal man.

"Sorry, I don't have any tea!" He said, turning to Marc.

"I don't drink tea," replied the Englishman.

"Milk and sugar for everyone?" Zahn asked.

"Have you got any arsenic?" Marc deadpanned.

The two Carls went ahead and set up the DTS XD10 media player that was going to decode the 5.1 track of the tape, and while they did Marc took a little stroll around the massive projection facilities that catered for the nine screens of the multiplex. The equipment for each screen occupied its own little cubby hole and all of them were accessible via tight stretches of corridor of varying lengths that connected them in a kind of twisting, maze-like configuration that Marc had to be careful not to get lost in. This was more or less the standard lay-out for a projection booth in a multiplex and Marc was no stranger to them by now, having poked around maybe as many as a hundred by then.

Marc liked projection booths; they were the unseen brain and control centre of all cinemas. With their giant, archaic 35 mm film reel projectors whirring around under industrial style fluorescent lighting they had a charming, oil-and-grease atmosphere to them. He usually liked the projection room staff as well; the working class, unsung heroes whose clockwork efficiency meant that Hollywood's million dollar blockbusters could magically fill a rectangular block of thin, perforated vinyl and transform the bland, stationary seating of a movie theatre into the best damn rollercoaster ride that ten bucks could buy.

With it being so early in the morning Carl Greenburg wanted to wait until at least 9 am before calling his New Jersey contact, rather than rudely waking somebody up on a Saturday and blowing their only chance of getting a helping hand, so Marc had plenty of time to chew his fingernails. As he walked around he was especially interested to see how the digital transition was settling in with the defiant 100–year-old film machinery it was destined to retire. In the brain region of many cinemas there was little sign of the technological surgery slowly underway, but at Regal the scalpels had been quicker to come out and here was a rare opportunity to see an entire multiplex begin the digital metamorphosis.

It was like a metallic skin graft slowly being applied to an aging, fleshy face. Each individual projection booth had a relatively early model of LCD video projector mounted on an improvised stand alongside its bigger, film counterpart, looking rather like a junior accessory, with trails of newly laid cables connecting them to an early generation server sitting on its own elsewhere in the building.

The pre-show digital advertising that formed the majority of Regal's digital content reached the server via underground fibre cables, scheduled and delivered from a central hub in Denver, almost as though sneaking in quietly to avoid upsetting the sensitive sanctity of the film machines, whilst an unseen satellite dish on the roof catered to live transmissions via decoder boxes tucked inconspicuously in racks in the corner of the booths. It was pretty clear that film was still the boss. It was as though the old could only give way to the new after coalescing in a state of superiority for a while, rather than concede its legacy overnight. It seemed the hi-tech gods would have no choice but to pace their revelations.

"My man in Jersey can hook us up with a PAL player. You're one lucky son of a bitch!" Carl Greenburg told Marc as he ambled back into the projection box of Screen 8.

Except they wouldn't be able to get their hands on the player that morning, however, since Carl's man in Jersey was apparently acting in a third party capacity and had to make a few calls himself. With early mornings and late evenings the only times available to test, given the scheduling of movies, they planned to shoot for Sunday evening at 10 pm to regroup at the theatre. In the meantime Carl would update Marc on the status of the player, which he would need to collect and return personally.

"Hey, I was ready to have one flown over from London!" Marc commented on having to play the courier. "I'll go anywhere to get it!"

With their new plan in place Marc spent the rest of the day walking nostalgically around the many streets he had got to

know so well years earlier, and before long he was back among
the expansive, grassy enclosures of The Great Lawn and Sheep's
Meadow in Central Park. It all looked exactly the same, like
nothing had changed, that the world outside may have been
getting more and more technological but in this quiet spot a
simple nature remained untouched, content to let everything else
go on as it pleased.

It spoke to him, of course, except now something was
jamming the transmission. A metaphorical reference for this
could already have been drawn in Zurich weeks earlier, when
W2 found its signal intercepted by an invisible P2P link. The
downlink and descrambling of the 24/7 spiritual signal was not
going to get projected without overcoming a few line of sight
issues of its own, it seemed, and the symbolical relevance of the
P2Ps, with their widely networked powers of mischief, left none
of the hi-tech gods with any illusion that the battle between
Good and Evil was over just because a new media age had
arrived.

*All distractions scrambled,* the Voice reported. *Business
priorities asserted.*

Early on Sunday afternoon Marc got a call from Carl
Greenburg with the address in mid-town where he was to
collect the digital Betacam tape player and it was with a big,
relieved smile that he showed up in the projection box later
with the piece of kit that he was a lucky son of a bitch to find
on a weekend. The two Carls helped to unpack it from its
flight case and rest it carefully beside the shiny, black DTS
XD10 5.1 media player. But as Greenburg checked the outputs
on the back of the machine his face betrayed renewed
exasperation.

"There's no digital audio output," he said shaking his head
and huffing, "just analogue. This is no good. They've given us
an older model. We can't play the 5.1 from this!"

The incensed New Yorker whipped out his cell phone and got
his New Jersey contact on the line in double quick time, insisting
that he'd made it clear what they needed but that they'd been
palmed off with something totally inadequate. From what Marc
could tell from reading Greenburg's grunts and nods the New

Jersey string puller sounded apologetic and would investigate and get back to him.

"He's sure he can deal with it but it won't be tonight," Carl told Marc. "Tomorrow you'll have to take this useless piece of junk back and pick up the right one."

"Is he absolutely certain we'll get what we need?" Marc pressed. "Tomorrow is the show and we won't have any more time to play with."

"He'll come through, trust me," Carl promised.

More grey hairs were making an appearance on Marc John's scalp but he could at least take some comfort from knowing that after the next twenty four hours it would all be over. Then he could weigh up all the pros and cons and hopefully arrive at a positive balance. That would be enough, just to survive whatever cataclysms were yet to surprise him and still come out ahead. It had been foolish to expect an easy closure to the whole thing anyway and he was almost impatient now for whatever final, parlous incidents remained, desperate to draw them out and see the back of them.

Monday began early at DuArt Film and Video Services on West 55th Street, where Erin had booked Marc in to make a back-up copy of the tape for the Regal screening. While he was there he was also able to have a look at the material and ascertain the three cue points that he, Brazil and Canada would need to synchronise to the exact frame. When he was happy with the start/stop/start points he noted the frame counts and got Jerome Merle in Brazil on the telephone first to make sure they matched up. Jerome ran the tape on his monitor while they were on the line together and Marc described precisely what he should be seeing at each cue point but, of course, there had to be a discrepancy!

"Marc, I'm not seeing exactly what you're describing even though we're at the same frame!" Jerome reported, specifically regarding the stop point at the end of the album performance.

How that could be the case when they had frozen their footage at supposedly the exact same frame was bewildering and even when Marc advised Jerome to jog the video backwards and forwards a few seconds the Brazilian still couldn't find the spot

Marc was talking about. He smiled. It was the first catch of the day.

"Okay, new plan ...," Marc fired, "scrap the tape. You and Canada are getting it all by satellite."

Jerome protested because it meant his cinemas would have to show the 4 × 3 picture format necessary to accommodate the Famous Players chain in Canada, but it simplified everything and the decision was made. In Manhattan Marc would have to stick with running a tape since Regal's Union Square theatre, the one location playing the 5.1 instead of the stereo, was not equipped with the right model of satellite decoder to receive a live feed of multi-channel digital audio. But this meant the only switchovers would therefore be down to him alone and this he was happy to shoulder.

He promptly booked extra satellite time with Verastar, a satellite vendor based in Washington DC, who had been contracted to provide the bandwidth for the Q&A segment, and told Erin the new plan was to give Brazil and Canada the entire show from Chelsea Studios rather than just the Q&A. It would mean making extra tapes for Erin to run at the studio, a main tape and a back up copy, which was all going to result in unbudgeted expenses, but it had to be done.

Marc personally ferried the tapes to Erin at Chelsea Studios on West 26th Street by the early afternoon where, meeting for the very first time, they greeted each other with a big hug and an affectionate showbiz-style kiss to each cheek. For her part, Erin had everything under control and adapted to the last minute changes with the kind of composed professionalism that Marc just hoped he was showing as well.

"Okay, so I'll be dialling into you to get in sync with when you start and switch," Marc told Erin.

"Are you sure there's nothing else you need?" Erin asked.

"Oh, I nearly forgot, do you have a camera by any chance?"

He explained he'd be racing back to the studio from the Regal theatre after the show for a photo with the star. The last email he'd sent before leaving the UK had been to Bowie's New York publicist, David Whitehead, asking if this would be okay and much to his delight Whitehead replied that it should be. Marc was determined not to miss his chance to finally meet the man but with all the rushing around he had forgotten to buy a camera!

Erin was happy to oblige and Marc bid farewell until later. By 3 pm he had switched the tape decks and parked the correct model in the projection box of Screen 8. He was going to have to cover the deck hire cost himself, since it was never in his arrangement with Sony for them to incur any expenses for the Manhattan screening, but he didn't mind. With DTS covering half the theatre hire it was still all going to work out as a bargain.

It was a waiting game now. He had the theatre all to himself from 6.30 pm onwards and the two Carls were due to show up at around 5.30 pm, with Visconti due at 7.30 pm to check the sound. A satellite test feed from Chelsea Studios was planned for 8 pm for thirty minutes for all cinemas and the show time set for 9 pm EST, or Eastern Standard Time. Sometime in the afternoon in BST land Julie Borchard called to check how things were going.

"A few things have changed on the technical side and we've incurred a few extra costs," Marc confessed. "There were issues with the tapes, it's all a bit convoluted, I don't know if you want me to go into it right now ..."

"No, don't worry, so long as everything's okay."

Marc assured her it would be and they agreed to talk on the following day, given that the five hour UK time difference would make it very early in the morning back in England by the time the show wrapped at around 10.30 pm EST.

"Marc, it's Tony, I'm in the lobby," Bowie's legendary record producer called to tell him on his mobile phone punctually at 7.30 pm.

"I'll be right down," Marc answered.

By then the projection box for Screen 8, which couldn't have been much bigger than four metres square and jammed with clunky film equipment, was even more packed as a result of several, extra faces having shown up over the course of the late afternoon. In addition to the two Carls there was the marketing director for DTS, Brian Caldwell, who had made a special trip

from Los Angeles, as well as Greenburg's all-important New
Jersey contact, who had made a special trip across the Hudson
River to see what they were up to. On the Regal side Jurgan
Zahn was on hand together with Angelo the chief projectionist,
who were jointly responsible for the management of the satellite
reception and video projector.

It was louder and busier in the booth than ideally it should
have been but, between all the parties, they had succeeded in
getting a beautiful picture on the cinema screen together with
the 5.1 audio blaring gloriously from the speakers. Marc told
them to leave everything running and that he'd take Visconti
directly into the auditorium to let him hear what they were
working with before bringing him up to the box to tweak the
EQ. Caldwell wanted to meet Visconti too and Marc was happy
to take the excited marketing man down with him.

After a quick photograph taken of the three men by
Caldwell's assistant they headed into the darkened auditorium
where the booming music had an immediate effect on Visconti,
who transformed into a kind of delicate sound reading
instrument. The virtuoso record producer proceeded to dart
quickly from one speaker to the next where he would pause, tilt
his head at a certain angle and then gently close his eyes to
absorb the euphonic data, his nostrils quite literally flaring as
though taking in the aroma of a freshly cooked dish.

Brian Caldwell took a seat and stretched out his legs as all this
went on, while Marc popped a stick of gum in his mouth to help
with the evening's first onset of nerves. None of it had really
seemed surreal until now, as Marc stood at the back of the
theatre watching Visconti bounding around between speakers
with almost operatic grace, perfectly silhouetted against the
shimmering glare of Bowie rocking away on the big screen.

In the projection box a short time afterwards a packed but
now hushed room reverentially respected Visconti's presence as
Angelo and the DTS duo dutifully catered to his wishes for how
the cinema speaker levels needed to be individually adjusted to
optimise the mix. The upshot was he basically wanted to lift
Bowie's vocals out of the centre channel a bit more and put
more bass in a few areas, although there were limits to what a

standard cinema sound system could manage. Visconti was used to being well treated, possibly even feared, and it showed. When the maestro could tell he had got the most out of the exercise he whirled abruptly round and strutted out like a king taking leave of his court, saying a rather succinct, emotionless thank you as he went. Nobody took it personally, of course, and it wasn't meant to be a tea party anyway.

"Well done, gentleman," Marc said to his crew, just in case anyone did feel a tad short changed on the gratitude.

They deserved the praise too. Once the theatre was clear at 6.30 pm the two Carls and the Regal team had got straight down to business, hooking up all the kit with methodical efficiency and keeping easily to the schedule of being ready for Visconti at 7.30 pm, as well as being in shape for the satellite test at 8 pm, which also went off without a hitch. The audience were let in at 8.30 pm and within five minutes there was hardly a seat empty.

Being a promotional exercise for Quantum Digital and DTS the entry was free, with admission vouchers being handed out at the box office to people who had pre-registered to attend. Two hundred and fifty vouchers had been reserved for Bowie fans to ensure that some of his American brigade got treated to the experience and once news of the show had been announced on his official website the allocation had been gobbled up almost immediately. The rest of the seats were taken by some of the band members and their friends, numerous Sony execs and whoever DTS had managed to attract from the press and cinema industry.

Just before 9 pm Marc dialled into Erin at Chelsea Studios from inside the projection box with his tape cued to start at the exact same frame as hers. All around him the crew were quiet and poised. It was a perfect moment to say something, a pep talk of sorts and he didn't care how corny it was going to sound either.

"Gentlemen, one day all cinemas will be digital and shows like this will happen at the push of a button," Marc started, "and we'll look back and remember what it was like at the beginning, in the pioneering days, when everything was so new and difficult

... but you should all feel proud, very proud ... because we're making history!"

"That was lovely," Greenburg reliably quipped in his thick New Yorker brogue. "Can I have a transcript?"

"Here we go ..." Erin alerted down the phone line.

Together Erin and Marc counted down from ten and as they did Angelo the projectionist faded out the house music and brought down the theatre's overhead lights while Carl Greenburg lightly rested his forefinger on the play button of the tape deck. His junior partner Carl Campbell, along with Regal's Jurgan Zahn, stood at the cinema sound processor ready to hit a specific button necessary to switch to the 5.1 output, while the saviour from New Jersey watched on in suspense over Marc's tense shoulders.

"Three, two, one ..."

The tape rolled and the picture shot brilliantly out onto the screen, except the audio suddenly decided to misbehave! For three or four seconds it popped and whizzed, similar to how a car exhaust pipe violently sputters when it's close to a breakdown. These awful aberrations were clearly heard exploding out of the cinema speakers, completely letting down the otherwise dazzling visual impact of the start of the show. After about five seconds it passed and the sound settled down to run in crystal clear synchronicity with the picture. Everyone in the projection box just stood there, motionless, speechless, silently praying the popping sound wouldn't suddenly re-occur.

"What the hell just happened?" Marc finally asked.

"Beats me," said Carl Campbell, "but it only lasted a few seconds, hopefully by the end of the show nobody will even remember it."

Marc darted out of the projection box and down to Screen 8 and poked his head inside to check out the vibe. He was still operating on the pros versus cons principle and had managed to keep his cool. Everything looked and sounded great in the theatre and plenty of bodies were bopping to Bowie's groove, so maybe the early shudder would not count for much.

*Damage limited,* the Voice assured him. *Situation stabilized.*

He checked the status with Brazil and Canada and was relieved to learn that everything was proceeding perfectly across their parts of the hemisphere, with all the theatres sold out and some fans even dancing in the aisles. He was able to reappear in the projection box in good enough spirits to smile. He was almost home and dry.

"Okay, counting down to the live feed ..." Erin said fifty two minutes later.

Marc was back in the box on the phone with Erin, with his team ready to switch the feed from the tape deck to the satellite receiver upon his command.

"We're live ..." Erin declared.

"Switch now!" Marc barked.

They switched. The screen went black – and stayed black.

"We're not getting it!" Angelo exclaimed.

Jurgan anxiously checked all the connections on the satellite receiver while Angelo fiddled with the inputs on the video projector, both men shaking their heads and muttering all sorts of maledictions as the sweat beads blistered.

"It's not the equipment, it's the signal ..." Jurgan finally said.

"Erin, what's going on with the signal?" Marc shot down the line.

"It's up and everyone else is getting it," Erin confirmed. "And I hate to say it but if you can't downlink in the next few minutes we'll have to drop you from the Q&A ..."

Meanwhile the packed house were sat facing a barren screen, along with one excited fan standing up next to the local host, anticipating that he would get to ask his question at some point. Marc didn't want to think about how many well tailored Sony figures had started to squirm!

"It's not the signal, keep checking the equipment," Marc urged forcefully. "We've still got a couple of minutes. Carl, is the tape cued for the encore?"

"I'm ready whenever you give the word."

His cell phone rang and it was Julie's assistant, who was inside the theatre and needed to know from Marc if the host should keep the fan waiting to ask his question or whether the tech problem was serious enough to put the segment in jeopardy. The dispirited Regal men looked clearly beaten as they turned to Marc and threw their hands in the air. All hearts were sunk.

"It's serious," Marc answered. "We're going straight to the encore."

Marc reluctantly gave Greenburg the nod and the show kicked back into life, at least with no pops or whizzes this time; not that this was much consolation. Nobody wanted to be the first to say anything and a dejected silence fogged the little room. Marc didn't want to run down to the theatre to check the vibe this time. Instead he just smiled wryly and walked out of the booth with no particular direction in mind.

Twenty minutes later when the final credits were rolling Marc was off in some quieter, unpopulated area of the projection backroom with his head down, pacing in a circle, wondering how it was that he could have made the trip to personally supervise the screening – whereas in every other city across the world a wholly remote style of management had been sufficient for a technically faultless performance – and yet it was here that the show had been struck with the most blows? It defied all logic.

# 9

# IT AIN'T OVER YET!

Marc John wanted heads – blood dripping, eyeball-bulging, freshly axed heads to hold up as the culprits responsible for the satellite fiasco at 800 Broadway. The fledgling Emperor was less Napoleonic now and more like Robespierre, the French Revolution's infamous, guillotine loving exactor of justice and terror! Sure, the buck ultimately had to stop with Quantum Digital but the bigwigs at Regal had some explaining to do.

"We accept responsibility, Marc," Dan Diamond sheepishly conceded, "the screw up on the satellite side was down to us."

It turned out the project manager assigned by Diamond to liaise with Marc on all matters had telephoned the satellite provider shortly before the live feed at 10 pm and instructed them to *alter* the satellite co-ordinates. The reasoning behind this had to do with bad weather reported to be swirling around the AMC-3 satellite, which the project manager judged would require a higher Forward Error Correction, or FEC, setting than the one Marc had previously specified.

FEC works by replicating certain bits of data in the transmission to give the receiver box more chance of extracting whatever binary codes might be most vulnerable to corruption in adverse weather conditions. It's not quite the same as sending the file twice but more a case of loading up on the weakest bits. The trade off is that *more* of the transmission bandwidth is taken up by the extra data as a result, which means a more heavily compressed and therefore weaker picture signal overall.

The trade off was always questionable as far as Marc was concerned and uniformly elsewhere around the world he had made the judgement to stick with a low FEC setting rather than decrease the bandwidth for the picture. He hadn't lost a single satellite feed as a result, until now when Regal took a different judgement without consulting with him on it.

"You know, when I explain all this to Sony Music it's just going to sound like I'm trying to fast talk my way out of trouble," Marc told Dan.

But Diamond was decent enough to agree to a conference call on the Wednesday morning before Marc was due to leave New York, where he admitted to Julie, Robert and Erin that his own project manager had interfered with the co-ordinates and that Regal was prepared to take responsibility for the problem. It was never clear if the adjusted FEC setting had been the cause of the signal failure or whether Jurgan and Angelo were never actually alerted to the change in the first place in order that they could have programmed the new digits into their receiver. At that point all everyone on the call could do was shrug, sigh and put it down as being "one of those things".

The wily Julie Borchard did Marc a favour, though, by suggesting to Dan Diamond that since Regal had effectively ruined the show wasn't Marc entitled to a refund on the theatre hire fee? Diamond, not wanting to aggravate the situation even further and not least mindful of building a smiley, happy relationship with a record label giant, agreed to this, keeping whatever reluctance he might have had diplomatically at bay.

Diamond's willing head on the chopping block helped to keep the pros and cons tipped just favourably enough in the right direction for Marc to fly out of JFK persuaded that he hadn't suffered more regrets than he could live with, although the mistakes still stung. He just hoped nothing got said about the problems in any US TV interviews Bowie was due to give! Leaving his beloved New York was less painful now that he had a few bad memories to put behind him, and he tried to focus as much as possible on the positives.

He reminded himself that the show had passed off beautifully in Canada and Brazil, including the Q&A segment, and even with the Manhattan mishap and extra costs Julie had assured him that all of Sony Music, as well as David Bowie himself, had judged the overall experience to have been well worth the effort.

Over fifty thousand people had seen the show on close to a hundred cinema screens in twenty two countries spanning five continents and, remarkably for a marketing exercise, the label actually *made* money. The average ticket price had been $12.

The media coverage had been enormous too. The album had shot to number one on the Billboard European Top 100 chart; reaching the top spot in the Czech Republic and Denmark, number two in France, Greece and Norway, number three in Austria, Germany and the UK and number four in Belgium and Italy. Julie had been given a standing ovation at an international marketing directors meeting in London and Robert assured Marc that they were sitting pretty. Did it really matter if a few nuts and bolts had fallen off along the way?

But something else that grated him was that he missed his chance to grab a photo with Bowie. Immediately after the show in Manhattan somebody had to make an announcement to the audience to explain what had happened and Marc somehow found the spine to do it, citing bad weather and being relieved to find the crowd a forgiving bunch. But by then Bowie had long since departed Chelsea Studios and even if Marc had found the nerve to still ask for a picture it would have been too late anyway.

Back in his office at the Odeon cinema in Aylesbury on Friday afternoon of that week the exhausted jet setter was busy trawling the web, copying and pasting as much positive feedback as he could find into a document he was drawing up for his meeting with the new Odeon boss, Ian Pluthero, which had been set for the following Monday.

"David pioneers again!" Melanie Kirkbride declared from Sydney, Australia. "The atmosphere was intimate and electric and David joined us live for questions – can't wait for the tour – God speed Down Under!"

"I just came back from the David Bowie live telecast at the Cineleisure cinema in Singapore," wrote Lai Pooi Yin. "David Bowie was in his sexiest outfit and looks 30 years younger. It felt like a real concert! By the way, where can I get his T-Shirt?"

Panegyric raves like these were exactly what his case for contract renewal needed and he would even read them over

and over so he could quote them by memory, not least to
make himself feel more triumphant than he otherwise did. He
didn't know if it was his own masochistic style of self-criticism
or whether he was truly undeserving but he just couldn't
shake off feeling like a failure. The feeling wasn't helped when
he happened to come across one, anonymous fan who had
posted comments that were not congratulatory at all, and
which challenged the observer to consider a very different
perspective ...

"I just spent $15 to help David Bowie promote an album!"
the fan started, identifying that he had seen the show in
Australia. "Here is technology that can bring large masses of
people together for a live, interactive experience and create a
feeling of global unity like we've never known before – but will
anything on a spiritual level come of it, or is it just going to be
about making money?"

Marc read it once and scoffed, scrolling down the page to
selectively fish for better morsels than those that were not
unconditionally fawning. But he couldn't shake off the
thoughtful critique and was soon muttering any number of
justifications to himself.

"Lots of people were happy to pay for the privilege of seeing
their idol live, what the heck is wrong with you?" he mumbled.
"These things cost money to put on for God's sake! You don't
get to see him in a stadium for free do you? Idiot! Utopian fool!
And who do you think you're talking to about spirituality, don't
you realise I'm the most spiritual man in the ..."

And then he paused, catching himself with what he was
saying. He tried to finish the sentence but couldn't and it
perplexed him.

*Refuse bait to analyse!* The Voice sharply instructed.

He had started to scroll back up the page to read the
comments again but stopped himself, shaking his head as
though wasting his time on something unimportant.

"This is a business," he continued to mumble, "you're
probably just some college drop-out anyway!"

*Better, better ...*

He scrolled back down and continued to pluck the more laudatory comments off the web but something about that particular comment continued to grind away at him in the back of his mind. Indeed, now should have been the exit point, the return to the revolution. He had a global network of cinemas at his command, all of them ready and eager to follow his lead on what to do next. He could have got away with trying something experimental, something daring. In those early days of digital cinema anything would have been tried at least once. The Bowie gig had laid the foundation and given him a world stage no less! Wasn't this the moment he'd convinced himself he was working toward all along?

But, again, he just wanted to strengthen his position a little bit more, maybe get a few more countries in the mix. The network could always be bigger, he started telling himself. Surely it would be foolish to start getting high minded now, just when things were taking off. The Voice hardly had to speak, by that point he was well programmed.

Ian Pluthero loved him! The Bowie show had been a spectacular commercial success for Odeon, with all six UK theatres sold out and fans euphoric throughout. Only *Pirates of the Caribbean* had taken more at the box office that night and this in the context of *Pirates* playing on some seventy or eighty screens and Bowie on just six!

"Imagine if we'd shown it on twenty screens," Marc said, "or a hundred!"

Pluthero didn't need telling. Odeon's marketing director Ron Hanlon was also present at the meeting and both were emphatically behind Marc John's continued efforts to drive the concept forward. There was just one little snag – which was that Ian Pluthero was not actually the permanent CEO but merely the *acting* CEO. He was there simply as a stop-gap while the Board assessed a shortlist of candidates to permanently replace Richard Segal.

Odeon was privately owned by venture capitalists, which at the time comprised a film distributor, a property group and a German investment bank, and the word on the grapevine was that the investors were looking to offload Odeon but wanted a top flight "name" at the helm to help the price tag. Pluthero apparently wasn't "name enough" and after doing his sales pitch Marc realised he would have to do it all again when the new man came in. But at least Ron Hanlon was now on his side, which was no small feat considering that the marketing department in general had never really warmed to digital cinema, preferring instead to concentrate on the movie side of the business.

"Film is what cinema is all about!" Ron had always said when goaded into doing something for one of Marc John's projects. "This digital stuff is just big TV!"

Big TV or not it was a hit when properly marketed, although Marc made sure not to revel in any self-righteous smugness. If Pluthero was in a revolving door situation the digital man needed all the friends at top level he could find, especially with his mentor and Odeon number two Barry Keward set to retire and his old ally from the film bookings department, Tony Giddings, also on his way out.

What Marc really needed now was another big event and quickly, something to reinforce his insistence that a corner really had been turned and that alternative content would finally start making Odeon some serious, regular money. He didn't have to wait too long. A few days after the Pluthero meeting he got a call from none other than IE Management, the handlers of Robbie Williams.

Williams had a music DVD release in the pipeline called *What We Did Last Summer*, which comprised a selection of performances from his extremely successful Knebworth dates from August, and IE wanted a glitzy, all-digital premiere at Odeon Leicester Square to match anything done by Hollywood, which Robbie himself would attend and introduce. Since the show was recorded in glorious high definition video and Odeon Leicester Square was already equipped with the best HD projector on the market at the time it was a perfect match of material and venue. With a watering mouth Marc promised to make it happen.

"I'll get a figure for the theatre hire," Marc told the marketing agency IE had drafted in to liaise with him. "On the technical side you can leave everything to me."

But if he thought Odeon's marketing department was anti-digital he was in for a double dose of it from the man being groomed as the new Head of Film Bookings, Craig Shurn, whose negativity toward the concept was so acute that Marc wondered if the grey-thatched celluloid lobby of the British Society of Cinematographers had him under remote hypnosis! Shurn was increasingly the man Marc had to deal with for all his digital bookings and initially his efforts to book the Square were roundly swatted away by an insistence that 20th Century Fox, who had the 2000–seat main screen booked months in advance, would never contemplate foregoing even a single performance.

"Can't we offer Fox compensation to give up the screen?" Marc argued. "We're talking about a Tuesday, not a weekend. There's nothing to lose in asking."

Odeon's loyalty to film distributors was understandable but, as Marc saw it, it risked compromising their bottom line overall as digital cinema gathered pace. It was as though the distributors mattered more to the bookers than the Odeon business itself – a bit like a maitre-de turning away high spending diners he might not recognise in favour of a few regulars who might only order the soup. Eventually Marc wrestled a figure of £5K out of the bookings department as a sum Fox could be persuaded to accept in return for giving up the screen time, which sounded extortionate but at least it was a breakthrough.

The typical venue hire fee charged by Odeon Leicester Square for premieres was also around £5K, but wanting to demonstrate that alternative programming was indeed a golden goose waiting to lay eggs galore he went back to IE with a total quote of £25K. Considering the blatant heist that SBE had tried to get away with just a few months earlier Marc knew this was loose change in comparison, not least when measured against the whopping £85 million paid to Williams by EMI Music for a five-album recording deal.

"If you can get twenty five grand for a premiere I'll faint!" One of the managers at Odeon Leicester Square told him.

He got the £25K and hoped none of the managers got hurt falling over! The event was set for November 18th and the contract was quickly drawn up and approved by Barry Keward.

"Boys, how would you like to be the exclusive digital 5.1 partner for a red carpet premiere of a Robbie Williams show?" Marc asked his DTS cohorts over coffee.

Marc stayed loyal to his audio chums and proceeded to convince IE about the merits of using DTS over Dolby, who were in the frame initially from having been involved with SBE. The show presented another opportunity to create a special cinema mix of the digital 5.1 soundtrack, which EMI Music A&R executive Chris Briggs certainly felt would be needed and, together with sound specialists Britannia Row, DTS worked out the necessary modifications to everyone's satisfaction.

Meanwhile the fallout from the Bowie success was attracting other Sony Music product managers with ideas for similar promotions, and just a few weeks ahead of the Williams premiere Marc organised a DVD screening of the classic, digitally re-mastered AC/DC concert *Live at Donington,* which ran at six Odeon theatres on a free admission basis, with Sony Music happy to hire the venues and promote the event via radio station partners.

Also, in early November, Marc put on an exclusive UK screening at Odeon Manchester of an Ultimate Fighting Championships tournament which had taken place live in Las Vegas a week earlier. A specially edited tape was flown over and, considering how a UFC show at the Royal Albert Hall in London in 2001 had attracted over 11,000 cheering people, Marc was convinced it was worth trying out on the big screen. At the time the UFC shows were not being aired on UK television and it was a deal Marc had spent six months putting together after meeting the UFC organisers during a trip to the ShoWest cinema convention in Las Vegas that spring.

Yet again he struggled to get it past the bookings people and the rank and file in marketing were just as lukewarm toward it. In the end Marc even had to ring around Manchester's local press personally in order to generate publicity, with the *Manchester Evening News* eventually picking up on it with a good sized article. He just hoped that whenever the new CEO was announced it would result in a few rear ends being kicked swiftly into line.

The Rugby World Cup, scheduled for December, was also considered worth trying and, with Carlton Screen Advertising always prepared to chase potential sponsorship deals, a meeting was arranged for Marc to make a presentation to the brewery group Fullers. A sponsorship deal in the high five figures was later agreed and live rugby was added to the growing portfolio. He was on a roll.

The Robbie Williams premiere was a hit, technically everything was perfect and the night was exciting as hell. Marc even found time on the night to roam around with a DVCAM camcorder to shoot some footage for posterity. Afterwards he enjoyed a fantastic time at the glamorous after-show bash at the Café Royal on Regent Street along with a few close friends he had managed to get on the guest list. The golden boy was glowing, not a hint of bronze in sight!

Away from the frenetic pace of his beloved career he kept himself in tip-top condition, determined not to squander his career potential by descending into the kind of romanticised nihilism that others might have succumbed to. He was no stranger to the local gym and his 5 foot 10 inch frame was kept trim at 155 pounds. Carbohydrates were minimal and he drank mineral water like it was running out of supply. He allowed himself the occasional weekend to drink hard and chase tails but flirting with self-destruction was something he firmly intended to avoid in order that he kept his rivals at bay and progressed higher up the ladder.

And love?

He probably wasn't helped in this department by the Victorian-era science fiction novelist H. G. Wells, who openly advocated a "free love" philosophy when it came to relationships. Marc had long been fascinated with Wells, particularly his uncanny ability to foresee and write about such things as atomic warfare, super-highways, overcrowded cities and television technology long before any of them became reality.

Maybe Wells was onto something with the idea of free love too, Marc had started to wonder sometime around his break-up with Joanne. Wells had many mistresses when he was married and even kept photos of his lovers in full view of his wife, Amy

Catherine Robbins, who questioned none of it. She even went out and bought baby clothes when, in 1908, Wells got one of mistresses, Amber Reeves, pregnant!

Was the highest nature of love therefore *not* to restrict it to one person? And that complications only arose when the unenlightened, primal instincts of jealously and possessiveness came into play? These were questions Marc couldn't help but feel compelled to ask and explore.

It was the right and wrong time to meet Ivonne, a beautiful German girl who deserved better than a scoundrel with a justification for everything. They met on the dance floor of the Café Royal at the Robbie Williams premiere after-show party and Marc would never forget how the swirling, multi-coloured lights seemed to all turn gold at once and swivel to focus spectacularly on just her.

Marc always wanted to meet a girl at a swish celebrity party and was actually on the look out for somebody famous like Beyoncé Knowles or Christina Augilera, seeing himself as elevated and dashing enough not to be out of place as one half of a glam couple. At one of the big movie premieres he'd attended at Odeon Leicester Square in 2002, for *Star Wars Episode II: Attack of the Clones*, he'd almost made a move on the American star Halle Berry, except she was with her husband at the time and Marc hadn't realised she was married in the first place, not that he wouldn't have settled for a discreet affair. The only reason he hadn't tried his luck with the beautiful star anyway had been because the British actor Michael York had tugged his arm to ask if the gorgeous group of girls he could see being photographed in the foyer were The Spice Girls.

"No, that's a group called Atomic Kitten," Marc answered, then thought about trying his luck with Jenny Frost instead, the sexiest member of the group, in his opinion.

But when he and Ivonne got talking there was something refreshingly ordinary about her. She wasn't in any way involved in the entertainment business and had managed to get waved behind the velvet rope by sweet talking the bouncers. What spirit she had! She was an *au pair* living with a family in Kensington on a one-year contract and didn't know what she was going to do afterwards. She was happy living in the moment and had an incredible vivacity about her. One of Ivonne's favourite things to do was roam around London's parks photographing flowers and Marc was particularly charmed by how much she adored Big Ben, which she also photographed a lot and affectionately referred to as "Biggie".

They started dating and spent many blissful afternoons strolling through parks that Marc barely realised were so glorious and serene once you got to know them, such as Battersea Park, St. James Park and Hyde Park. And when they visited Biggie they would usually take in the view from along the Embankment across from the Houses of Parliament, where Marc would vaguely remember running for election once upon a time.

He cheated on her of course. He hoped she would dump him because he wasn't ready to change and he hardly thought twice about cancelling dates at the last minute or putting business first as a rule. But she stuck with him and before long if his eyes were tempted to stray he would start to feel guilty. He hadn't felt guilty about anything in a very long time. Maybe Halle Berry had missed her chance.

"It sounds like love!" Joanne said during one of their coffee chats.

"Love ...?" he wondered, dwelling on the word.

"Yes, love. Have you forgotten what it is?"

It set him thinking ...

"You seem distracted," Robert Young said to him shortly before Christmas when they met over a drink in the lounge bar of the Le Meridian hotel in Piccadilly.

Robert was back in the UK on business and the pair always took the opportunity to meet face to face whenever they could. They were partners now after all.

"I don't know what it is," Marc replied, "maybe I'm just tired, I haven't had a holiday in years!"

"Then take a break, you're not a machine!"

*Wanna bet?*

But he didn't want to slack off during the transition of chief executives at Odeon. Even if a new boss wasn't installed by the time his contract was due for renewal at the end of December somebody else at Odeon was going to have to make a decision about it and it had to be positive.

Meanwhile Robert had been making progress in negotiations with Universal Music Group about the idea of doing a cinema gig with the Irish rock band U2 as part of the launch for their next album, which was due out in the autumn of 2004.

"Let's do a million people!" Robert had boldly said. "And go live everywhere, even if fans have to turn out at 4 am in some parts of the world."

U2 were the biggest band in the world and hitting a million people would be sensational. The fee on a gig that big wouldn't be bad either. Marc John estimated that, if he could succeed in reeling off an average of six gigs a year, he would be a millionaire within three years! Not only that but his temporarily nameless business partnership with Robert Young also looked set to become the pre-eminent live distributor as digital cinema blossomed, the Google of its kind no less.

And the revolution? What revolution?

As January 2004 came around Ian Pluthero was still the acting CEO at Odeon but it probably fell to either Barry Keward or Ron Hanlon to make a decision on Marc John's contract. To his delight and relief an extension was offered which was open-ended to self-renew every three months unless terminated by either side not less than thirty days before the start of each quarterly period. He would have preferred an open-ended contract that self-renewed every twelve months, rather than quarterly opt-outs being possible, since this didn't exactly offer the best feeling of job security, but expected he could renegotiate later in the year once the new CEO was installed.

At least now he knew he'd get the chance to build on his progress. Even though Odeon had yet to invest in any digital kit Marc was continuing to keep them ahead of UCI with his persuasiveness in getting content providers to cover the hire of LCD projectors, which he argued could be justified as a marketing cost. And, in cases where admission was charged, the box office share to the content provider helped to offset costs even further.

Nothing was heard from UCI, BT, SBE or any of the other digital cinema wannabes. Even the likes of Boeing and Technicolor were faltering, laying off their digital cinema project managers and lamenting how they couldn't prise a way into a tough, new market. But Quantum Digital was still there, going from strength to strength, having outlived them all. At one point a couple of former business development managers from Boeing and TDC were even calling Marc to inquire if Quantum Digital had any vacancies!

By the time he and Robert made a stylish, big screen slide presentation to executives from Universal Music Group in mid-February 2004 for their proposed U2 cinema event, which included clips of the Bowie show as well as a neat montage of other alternative content successes, Marc couldn't have been any more on top of the world unless he went out and bought the best damn ice palace the North Pole had to offer!

In his time honoured tradition of reviewing his performance in meetings over a steaming latte Marc John would invariably end up in a coffee house somewhere in the West End, scribbling notes and mentally lashing himself if anything had not been up to par. Usually this was strictly private time but before long he couldn't resist inviting Ivonne to come and meet him, as she was usually free from 10 am to 2.30 pm most days once the eight-year-old boy she was looking after had been dropped off at school.

He rationalised the diversion from his business mindset as taking good advantage of her flexible schedule and being more convenient for him than travelling back to Aylesbury and then coming back into London in the evening when she'd be free after six most evenings, although he started doing that before long as well.

The Starbucks in Leicester Square is where they met most often and between finishing his self-appraisals and excitedly anticipating her arrival he would think more and more about love, wondering if he was *in it*, wondering what it was and wondering how he could have lived without it for two full years!

"What happened to me?" he quietly asked himself one day.

And that chastening comment from the fan Down Under would rear itself in his mind again, except not merely as he remembered reading it but coming fully to life in the imagined form of a ranting, Aussie-accented barracker, made flesh and in his face, not content with his original comments and hyperbolically extending on them!

"G'day mate, what's ya problem then eh? Ya got a revolutionary technology here without the frigging revolution! C'mon mate, sort it out won't ya?"

*Caution! Caution! Restrain schizophrenic circuitry!*

"And you can shut ya trap too, ya micro-processed little termite! Ya got me cross as a frog in a sock! Now c'mon mate, I don't mean to be a wowser but ya gotta do a yewy and soon!"

It wasn't just a rambunctious, imaginary Aussie who got in his face to remind him of a few things. His friends in Aylesbury, as well as total strangers who remembered his face from the newspaper, would often ask him what had happened to the Aylesbury Film Company and why wasn't he making any more socially relevant movies? Usually he'd just say he was busy setting up a digital network in cinemas around the world so he'd have a distribution platform for future movies and that the AFC hadn't been killed off. Then he'd walk away with all their faces and questions swirling around inside his head, their features becoming exaggerated and grotesque in their disapproval of his self-delusion, as though his neglected creative imagination was staging a revolution of its own.

"I've got to get back to making movies at some point," he'd say to Ivonne when they'd talk about their hopes and dreams, the way couples do in the beginning. "I thought I was an artist. I used to have dreams of changing the world ..."

But whenever he came close to realising the true depth of his transformation his precious career would inevitably requisition him back to the empire building. Like so many people sucked into the corporate vortex he seemed beyond the Spirit's rescue.

In May Odeon finally announced its new Chief Executive, a man named Tim Schoonmaker, who Marc nervously awaited some info on. With a prominent background in digital radio and digital television the New York-born, former Chairman of Emap Advertising apparently had the street cred the investors were looking for, as well as a promising pro-digital pedigree. Indeed, figures within Odeon were telling Marc he couldn't have hoped for a better boss.

"I'll set up a meeting," Ron Hanlon promised, "I think you'll have a lot in common,"

*How perfect!*

Marc was ready for it. The month of May 2004 already had two fresh successes to shout about, the first being a music DVD launch of a Tori Amos concert titled *Welcome to Sunny Florida* and the other a groundbreaking promotion for Canon digital cameras which saw "wi-fi" technology used in a cinema for the first time.

The Canon project was called *Picture Yourself on the Big Screen* and involved audience members in a dozen or so cinemas around the UK having their pictures taken in the foyer with the new Canon IXUS 500 digital camera and then seeing the pics enlarged on the cinema screen just seconds later; all made possible via a wi-fi transfer of the pictures to a laptop in the projection box which ran them through a neat software programme, before outputting them to a video projector in near-instantaneous time. It had a real "wow factor" about it and was due to net Odeon a hefty sum in a promotional deal brokered by CSA.

Marc was also in talks with Universal Music Group, separately to the U2 proposition, to programme a series of music videos ahead of when the advertising and trailer reels ran; when audiences were typically shuffling in and the screen would otherwise be dead or, at most, showing outdated slides via an antiquated carousel. Pre-show music videos would be an entirely new concept and the potential to attach a sponsor and drive additional, new revenue was also demonstrated when the Ben & Jerry's ice cream brand came to the table prepared to open their wallet.

And by the late spring his digital cinema efforts had been given a particularly significant boost, when new government legislation made it compulsory for cinemas to cater for more disabled customers by offering a minimum number of film screenings with sub-titles for the deaf and audio description headphones for the hearing impaired. This had resulted in government funding via the UK Film Council for Odeon to acquire twenty six high quality LCD video projectors, similar to those he had used for the Bowie show, to project the sub-titles from disc over the film-projected movies.

Since the kit was only going to sit idle outside of meeting the quota for the disabled screenings Odeon's Head of Sound and Projection, Paul Schofield, was quite happy to approve Marc John's utilisation of it for alternative programming. This was a major development, meaning a lot more content providers could be won over to the concept without projector hire costs potentially discouraging their interest, as was the case on several occasions.

Fortunately Schofield was an avid supporter of the digital agenda and someone Marc had become close with since joining Odeon. With Richard Segal, Tony Giddings and Barry Keward all gone, and even Ron Hanlon expected to bow out before long, Paul Schofield was going to be the last of the old guard with whom Marc had forged vital ties.

By the end of May Marc had still not been slotted into the new chief's diary and Ron Hanlon, as expected, had dropped down to working just one day a week in a phasing out period, making it harder for Marc to nail down an appointment with Schoonmaker as a result. Given who was left at Odeon to influence Schoonmaker's outlook on digital cinema Marc desperately wanted to state his case sooner rather than later, feeling that other voices were not likely to stay quiet with their opinions.

Ron's successor, for example, a man named Luke Vetere, was just as fiercely anti-digital as Craig Shurn who, as expected, had assumed full control of the bookings department once Tony Giddings stepped down. Between them they had the power to stymie all things digital. But if Marc could just get ten minutes to work on Schoonmaker he didn't believe their ascension to power would matter a hoot, except there was just one problematic consequence. They fired him.

In early June, when Marc went along to see the pair of freshly crowned princes to detail the next six months of his digital activity, he was told that *they* were his immediate superiors following the retirement of Barry Keward and that, in their judgement, digital cinema was not worth pursuing any longer.

"We're cancelling your contract," Shurn told him flatly.

Marc was stunned. The Voice froze. Nothing seemed real for about five seconds. Finally Marc thrust some words of his mouth just to deny his dagger wielders the satisfaction of seeing him bleed.

"Well, there's still another three months to run on my contract before the exit clause can be exercised," he said, recovering from the shock with a steady enough tone, "you've just missed the notice period to opt out during the present quarter, so are we at least going to see out the projects I've got going on between now and then?"

Shurn frowned and referred to a copy of the contract that he had in front of him, checking through it for the termination clause. As he did so Marc took the temporary respite to try composing himself. Internally he had gone to pieces. The Odeon contract and the credibility the position gave him had been absolutely invaluable to his career, and the sizeable fee paid as a retainer was his financial lifeblood. Quantum Digital on its own, for all its potential, was still very much a sideline and even in his partnership with Robert Young there was a long way to go before life without Odeon was going to be affordable. As the reality of what was happening began to sink in he started to get very scared.

"I'll need to get back to you on your remaining period of service," Shurn finally said. "As for whatever you're working on now we can set up a handover meeting where you can give Luke all your contacts and project details and he'll decide what to take forward."

They hadn't even offered him a drink. No tea, coffee or even water and right now Marc was desperate to relieve his mouth of its awful dryness before it debilitated him from forming sentences. The lack of basic courtesy was evidently down to the fact that they wanted it over quickly. Shurn sat back and folded his arms as though signalling that the meeting was over as far as he was concerned. Vetere was at least decent enough to apologise for the sudden nature of his dismissal and Shurn mumbled something about downsizing the workforce being necessary for the sake of making the balance sheet more attractive to prospective new owners as well.

"But I haven't even met Tim Schoonmaker yet," Marc said, "I'd like to have that opportunity before I see out my term."

"Tim's been briefed on digital cinema," Shurn replied, "and we're in charge of that now, so our decision is final. There's nothing else to say about it."

And that was it. The meeting had lasted no more than five minutes when Marc had come prepared with an agenda to take up at least an hour. As he walked out onto the street a whole slew of arguments were exploding in his head that he wished he had taken a stand and countered with. Sacking him made no sense. Digital cinema was the future and he had put Odeon further ahead in the new marketplace than any other exhibitor in the world, including the mighty Regal in America. And he had barely got started! Were they nuts?

But then he was pleased that he hadn't argued his case because it would only have made him look desperate and pathetic and that was probably what they wanted anyway, he imagined, so they could flex their muscles and revel in telling him that they were calling the shots now. How he seethed and wished for a way to deal with them in swift, Robespierre fashion, the way he had with others.

"There must be a way around those scheming swines!" he muttered to himself as he crossed the street, stubbornly refusing to accept that his tenure at Odeon had really come to an end. "It ain't over yet boys!"

Getting over the shock of it in a quiet corner of a bistro, the deposed potentate began plotting how to counteract his foes and wondered if he should run out and buy Sun Tzu's *The Art of War,* remembering how the ancient military tactician had been artfully quoted by Michael Douglas in the movie *Wall Street*, telling his protégé Charlie Sheen that "every battle is won *before* it is fought!" Words to heed, Marc told himself as he set about formulating a campaign to neutralise his opponents.

Before anything else, he thought, every military consideration must first assess its alliances. He couldn't think of any modern wars where allies had not played a crucial part somewhere or other. He had Paul Schofield on his side as well as Ron Hanlon, although the latter was the equivalent of a Belgium compared to Schofield's France by that stage. Alliances determine strategy, he mused, and without strong enough pacts there couldn't be a battle plan, because something else that real warfare had shown was that wars are not necessarily over when the fighting stops. The alliances have to be strong and committed enough to keep the enemy subdued because an enemy is *never* beaten, just silenced. If Hanlon was being phased out then Belgium wasn't worth its place on the map. Was France alone big enough?

"Paul, you'll never believe what just happened ..."

Schofield was indeed surprised by the news and was gracious enough, as expected, to ask Marc if there was anything he could do to help? This was just what Marc wanted to hear, since the best alliances are always those that are volunteered and not coerced. But how was he to use Schofield? He didn't have a plan yet and suggested to his good friend that they talk again in a few days after he had the chance to mull over the situation and clear his head.

Next he decided to call Hanlon anyway, just to see if the departing executive might have some ammunition value, even if limited.

"I had no clue this was brewing, Marc," Ron said when told the news, sounding genuine enough. "Certainly nobody came to me for an opinion and I actually thought Tim's secretary had called you already to set an appointment."

There was little Ron could offer, especially since he had already passed along Marc John's details to the chief and that Craig and Luke were now supposedly his immediate superiors. All he could do was to suggest that Marc email Schoonmaker directly to politely request a meeting so he could at least be given the opportunity to make his case in person rather than be discharged without so much as a five-minute exchange of views.

It was a good idea but the timing had to be right. Perhaps Marc would send the email just before Paul Schofield was due to have his own meeting with the new boss and have Paul vouch

for him as an asset to the company, thereby leaving Schoonmaker less disinclined to give him a hearing. Yes, that seemed
like a fine strategy to start with.

Beyond this initial sortie he also had the three-month period
left to run on his contract before the opt-out clause could be
exercised and, no matter what Craig Shurn had said about
checking into it, technically and legally he was going to remain
Odeon's Head of Digital Cinema until the end of September.
During that time he had plenty of other projects in the pipeline
that could still be brought to fruition to win over Schoonmaker
in the event that the planned email and weight of Schofield's
influence wasn't enough.

In fact, his meeting just before the sacking had been with
Warner Vision, with whom he was in advanced negotiations to
distribute, across all twenty six of Odeon's newly equipped
digital sites, a music DVD due for release in July from the
legendary rock group The Who. Warner Vision was so keen on
the idea of cinema launches that, if all went well with The Who
screenings, they were prepared to supply plenty more product
on a regular basis.

He was also close to launching an interactive games
competition network across the same sites in conjunction with
the London PR firm Kazoo, whose clients included top games
manufacturers such as Activision and Lucas Arts. And with the
Carlton Screen Advertising sales force now fully engaged in
chasing sponsors for all these special events, on top of the box
office takings and venue hire deals, Marc John just couldn't
foresee all this failing to impress the man who mattered at
Odeon.

Yes, he absolutely had a solid enough strategy for survival
and, slowly, the awful shock and sickening terror he had felt less
than an hour before was gradually brought under his firm
control. He was Napoleon again and suddenly relishing the
prospect of battle. After all, he reasoned, the first casualty of
war must never be one's own morale.

A week later he went back in to see Luke Vetere to hand
over all his project files but stressed he did not want to
abandon the responsibility of ensuring that progress was made,

given the pledges he had given to the content providers and the amount of time he had spent forging so many professional ties.

"Besides, if I'm under contract for another three months surely you'd want me working and not sitting on a beach somewhere," Marc reasoned.

Craig Shurn was also sitting in on the meeting and had his steely eyes peeled to the contract in question throughout. Finally he looked up and told Marc they wanted to cancel the contract with immediate effect rather than retain him for the duration.

"You want to cancel now even though you're obligated to pay me until September?" Marc asked.

"Well, actually we don't want to pay you either," Craig answered, "if we're releasing you now we think it's fair that you waive what we owe you."

*Negative! Ditto! Negative!*

"Sorry, that's not going to be acceptable," Marc replied, amazed that they had the nerve to even suggest it.

Then Craig leaned in ominously and narrowed his eyes, clearly wanting to stick a little emphasis on his next bit of tact.

"Down the line you might need to be in our good books if you plan to distribute stuff as an independent, which presumably you'll continue to do as Quantum Digital," Shurn said. "If you force us to keep to our payment obligation you might not find us so friendly ... "

Well, well, well, Marc thought. It seemed the little princes had been working on their own strategy while he had been away working on his! Neither of them could have been much older than their early thirties, same as Marc, but clearly they saw themselves as old pros when it came to this type of manoeuvring. The plotting pair kept calm enough though. The atmosphere may have turned ugly but nobody was getting excited. It was almost as though the duo had seen so many laid back, sinister caricatures from all the movies they'd exhibited that some of it had rubbed off!

"Are you blackmailing me?" Marc asked.

"We're just saying you need to think about your future," Shurn answered.

But money aside Marc needed to stay in the job. If he was squeezed out now and forfeited his remaining three months his strategy would be shot to hell. He wouldn't get the chance to impress Schoonmaker and Luke Vetere would either quash his projects or ride on the back of them and take the credit. And there was no guarantee Shurn would do business with him again even if he did quietly walk away. These boys were better at this than he anticipated and had to be handled very carefully indeed.

"Okay, I'll think about it," Marc said finally, with a smile.

"When do we get your answer?" Luke asked.

"Well, for now assume that my position hasn't changed, just for clarity's sake," Marc answered, cautious against anything being purposely misconstrued. "I'll get back to you in a week and tell you if it's changed."

The following week was the start of the annual Cinema Expo trade fair in Amsterdam and Luke and Craig were both planning to attend. As it happened Marc had already booked his flight and hotel as well, which he did weeks ahead of their fateful showdown. Still, it was as good a place as any for them to meet one last time to settle the matter, and it gave Marc some critical breathing time to reassess his strategy.

He still had a bolt to shoot with Paul Schofield and when he found out the date for Paul's meeting with Schoonmaker he timed his email to the chief to coincide the day before. Paul reliably made a few, positive remarks about Marc John's work and the potential of digital programming, but understandably Paul had his own department and position to think about, so it was never going to be more than thirty second's worth of praise at most.

It wasn't enough. When Schoonmaker replied to Marc's email he copied Craig Shurn on it, telling Marc that Craig was in charge of digital cinema now and that Shurn should be his first point of contact for the remainder of his service. His campaign was flagging!

He had to think beyond September now. Even if he saw out his term he was unlikely to change anyone's mind and get his dismissal reversed. He couldn't imagine what the little princes had said to the CEO to so thoroughly repel any chance he had of getting through the door but whatever it was it had worked. He had to make some moves to ensure that he at least stayed employed in the industry. That would mean switching flag allegiances altogether and the formerly unthinkable prospect of asking UCI for a job suddenly had to be considered.

Gerald Buckle's boss Justin Ribbons, whom he remembered meeting the previous year at Cinema Expo, was quick to respond to a quietly and selectively circulated press release that Marc issued announcing his imminent departure from Odeon. Ribbons emailed to say that if Marc was planning to be in Amsterdam for the trade fair then perhaps they should meet for a chat.

Marc was pleased to see the bait taken and scheduled his meeting with the UCI boss to take place just a few hours ahead of his final face-off with Odeon. If UCI offered him a contract maybe he would jump ship from Odeon straight away after all and then try to hold Shurn to his word about being approachable in the future. It could yet all work out in his favour.

"Let's get straight down to business," Ribbons said at the meeting. "We know what you're capable of and we're interested to have you. What sort of terms did you have with Odeon?"

Marc liked his point blank style and came back in matching fashion, laying out his fees and expenses and the general remit he wanted. Basically he wanted exactly the same role he had at Odeon, and promised to blow his former employer away and put UCI at the forefront of digital cinema instead. Justin could well imagine the revenge angle converting nicely into singing cash registers and made the commitment right there and then to hire him. There was just one snag. Justin would need to hold off on formally producing a draft contract until the status of their ownership was clearer. UCI were coincidentally also up for sale, just like Odeon, and the new owners were similarly not yet known.

"It's not ideal to sign new contractors in a transitional period," Ribbons told him, "I'm pretty certain I'll be in a position to formalise this once I've spoken to the new Board and explained the digital case, so can we just sit tight for a few weeks?"

Ouch! A few weeks was a long time for Marc John right then. In less than thirty minutes he was meeting the boys from Odeon and suddenly the hand of cards he wanted to play had been shoved back in the deck!

"Sure, I can appreciate the situation and that's fine," Marc replied, with no choice in the matter.

A short time later on the way to the patio deck, where countless industry types could be found huddled under umbrella hooded tables talking tech lingo and drinking juice, Marc had perhaps ninety seconds to get his strategy in order. Did he take a chance on UCI delivering the promised contract and bow out of Odeon on repairable terms, forfeiting three months pay that he did actually need? Or did he stick with the sure money and risk alienating the UK's biggest exhibitor, whom he might need to call on at some point even if he was hustling for a rival?

As he stepped out onto the deck and weaved his way through the throng of suited bodies crowding the cement he came across plenty of familiar faces from various companies around the world that he'd either worked with or met a few times. There was no shortage of quick hand shakes and back slapping as the established industry figure made the obligatory stops to say, yes, everything was going great and, yes, he looked forward to catching up over a cocktail in the West End sometime and, yes, he had plenty of projects to talk to them about. And it was painful as hell, nobody realising the downfall he was suffering at the hands of a pair of ruthless assassins!

Finally he came to Shurn and Vetere and sat down across from them. They all leaned in somewhat, mindful that private matters were not overheard by ears that were known to swivel around like highly sensitive radars at conventions such as this.

"Well?" Shurn asked.

"I've always worked hard for Odeon," Marc started, "and digital programming has proved to be a winner, so it's baffling that I've been treated like I've done something wrong."

The Odeon pair looked sympathetic enough to the comments and Marc knew he needed to take the moral high ground, if he could get it, because his decision was not going to please them.

"So I've decided I can't just drop everything and be dismissed as though guilty of some hushed up crime. That's what leaving now would feel like, so I plan to see out my contract and the question now, I suppose, is how do you want to use my time?"

They looked surprised but couldn't do a thing about it. They didn't appear to have a counter-strategy lined up either, and it was awkwardly left that one of them would call Marc in a week about how they intended to use him for the remaining three months. In the meantime they wanted him to take the week off and not worry about any of the projects he'd handed over. That suited Marc fine. He needed the break anyway.

Later that evening in his hotel room he called Ivonne and gave her the update. He had more or less accepted that his Odeon days were over but was quite optimistic about the UCI contract. By then the couple had been dating for six months and had even started talking about getting an apartment together in London. Ivonne's *au pair* contract with the family in Kensington was due to expire in August and originally she planned to return to Germany to her family's home near Bremen. But they had become so close by then that the idea of being so far apart became unthinkable and Marc always assured her that on his salary alone they'd be okay in London. Despite his ousting nothing in his personal life had to suffer – provided Justin Ribbons didn't back out of his pledge.

A week later Craig Shurn called to tell Marc that Odeon had decided to pay him up until September as contractually agreed but that his services would not actually be required on an active basis during that period. In other words they were paying him off to simply quit right then and there. It was a totally unexpected move and Marc didn't know what to make of it. But with UCI in the wings he was less inclined to fight for his right to go out in a blaze of glory and in the end he just shrugged and accepted it.

It wasn't actually a bad deal, he thought. If he signed with UCI he'd start on their payroll whilst still drawing income from Odeon. Not a bad situation at all! He could already feel the career hungry pangs start to twitch in his gut again and couldn't wait to get down to business and show Odeon what idiots they were to toss him out. But then the most unlikely thing in the world happened. The same investment firm that bought UCI *also* bought Odeon! And this threw everything into uncertainty as far as Marc John's rebound back into the limelight was concerned.

"This could mean both chains merge and jobs get lost," Justin Ribbons had to confess when following up on the contract offer. "It could mean the film booking and marketing departments at Odeon take over the running of UCI ... with everything up in the air I just can't proceed with the contract, my own job might not be safe!"

Marc couldn't believe it. There were very few examples, if any at all, of a venture capitalist buying not one but two major cinema chains at the *same* time. And with Odeon already the largest in the market, its acquisition of UCI as well was surely going to fall foul of monopoly rules. It was an unprecedented, stunning swoop into the exhibition sector by the billion dollar-backed private equity firm Terra Firma. It left Marc completely on the outside, with no way into UCI and no way back to Odeon. Unless, of course, he went directly to Terra Firma and pulled off a career best sales pitch ...

"Yes, that's what I'll do!" the defiant careerist told his girlfriend. "This still ain't over yet!"

"Tell me how much you can make us from this digital stuff?" Lorenzo Levi at Terra Firma asked.

They were sat in an elegant, high floor Board room at the Terra Firma headquarters at 1 St Martin's-le-Grand in London in late October, after Marc had finally prised an opening with them after six weeks of gentle solicitation. Levi was a business director with the firm, responsible for the digital strategy across both cinema chains and was joined in the meeting by Joe Sinyor, the company's finance director.

By then Tim Schoomaker had surprisingly quit his post as Chief Executive, which gave Marc precisely the angle he needed to justify seeking a meeting at Board level given that no replacement had yet been announced. He was open about his former ties to Odeon and they didn't have a problem hearing him out. He probably had ten minutes maximum to make a dent.

"Well, we're talking about alternative programmes not movies, because with digital movies it'll be the studios reaping the financial benefits, not cinemas," Marc began, "but with things like sports, music and video games I think in the first year we could pull in anywhere from a hundred to two hundred thousand."

"Is that it?" Levi shot back incredulously. "If you told me half a mil or close to a mil I might buy into it. But a few hundred grand hardly makes it worth it!"

"These are early days," Marc countered, somewhat taken aback, "digital cinema is the future but nothing's going to happen overnight, it's all about making steady but sure progress."

"Not for me," Levi said. "We deal in a different set of figures to what you're talking. I'm really disappointed you didn't say a mil."

Terra Firma had paid £400m for Odeon and £183m for UCI and what became instantly apparent to Marc was that, as a venture capitalist, Terra Firma was in the cinema game for a quick profit with an exit strategy probably planned within three-to-five years. Whilst this type of turnaround period was not abnormal in the VC market it was probably the worst thing in the world for the proper nurturing of alternative programming.

"But we are interested to try things so let me talk to a few people within UCI and Odeon and we'll get back to you," Levi said.

Marc laughed and had to say something.

"I can already tell you what you'll hear from Odeon and it won't be positive!"

"We call the shots, Marc," Levi assured him. "We'll listen to different views and make our own judgement."

But Marc could hardly imagine his old foes – upon hearing that he had gone over their heads – would react too kindly to the prospect of him making a spectacular, Board-backed return. No, he thanked Levi and Sinyor for their time knowing that, between their hopelessly unrealistic profit targets and the animosity still permeating certain corridors in Leicester Square, there really was no way back.

Over his post-meeting latte he didn't even bother reviewing his performance. He had tried every manoeuvre possible and had failed. He was burnt out now and even somewhat disillusioned. He thought he was poised to become the Irving Thalberg of digital cinema, and indeed had come so far, yet everything was collapsing.

He still had his partnership with Robert Young but even that was stuttering. Sony Music went on to merge with BMG and the inevitable reshuffling meant that Julie Borchard and several other contacts vital to their relationship at Sony moved on. Universal Music Group ended up passing on their cinema event proposal for U2, and every one of the projects Marc had handed over to Luke Vetere were left to drift as Odeon turned its back on all his developments, leaving content providers disgruntled and with little interest in talking to Marc when he later tried to rekindle a dialogue. To top it off another potential rival had entered the fray and from the most unexpected of places ...

"Some people are going around saying they can do all the things Quantum Digital can do," Robert Young told him, tipping him off. "And you need to be careful with this lot because they're actually part of your own gang!"

"You're kidding, who is it?"

It was none other than DTS, the 5.1 audio specialists who Marc had stayed loyal to despite rivals Dolby jockeying for position at every turn. He had to laugh, crying could wait.

"I'm going to take that break now, Robert," he said. "I think you'll find my mobile phone switched off for quite a long while."

Looking in on the shell of the man could tell us no more now, as he withdrew further and further into that shell trying to figure out exactly what had happened to his life. Finally he was plunging into the deep and being held there, finding not darkness but truth. And as I started to come out of a fever that had lasted almost three years, uncurling my fingers from the grip of a bed I had somehow made for myself, it felt like regaining consciousness after an incredibly long hallucination. What had I become? And could I ever get back to being the man I was before?

# 10

# THE STARDUST SETTLES

My first reaction was to think I could do something positive with the experience of losing myself the way I did. I could write a script, play or a novel, finding my creative self again but drawing from reality this time and showing how easy it is to be seduced so unwittingly by the forces of ambition and power. Even as a man with ideals that had been ingrained over many years the seduction still found a way in. Didn't others need warning, no matter if they thought they didn't?

But the idea of it excited me so much that I quickly realised that similarly dangerous forces of ambition were driving me to contemplate the undertaking in the first place! I think it was when I started to especially regret not getting that photograph with David Bowie in New York City, because it would have made such a great coup as a picture to send out with press kits, that I knew the fever was still licking at me with a few defiant, dying flames.

How I chased Julian Stockton for a chance to get that photograph! I even told him I'd fly to New York at a moment's notice at whatever time might be convenient for his star to grant me just a minute for the snap. But Bowie had been taken ill with heart trouble in Germany over the summer of 2004 during the *Reality* tour and Julian said requests like mine were firmly off limits while he was recovering. I understood, of course, but it only made me regret that missed opportunity even more.

A book seemed the best medium for the depth I wanted to explore, although a lot of literary agents I emailed about the project advised I should concentrate on telling a behind-the-scenes, tabloid-level kind of story and not bother with all the personal, spiritual stuff. While others remarked that "there's always a bit of money in the spiritual game" – which in both cases left me wondering if I could succeed with a story that people didn't perceive as being nakedly exploitative, whichever direction I took?

Over my steaming lattes, free from career distractions, I now sat down to think about how I was going to craft a worthwhile story, somewhat concerned that the book publishing world was probably just as much of a commercial machine that gobbles people up as the machine I had just been spat out of. It made me wonder if a person's art can ever flourish without its integrity eventually being compromised. This hadn't happened to Bowie but it had happened to me.

Not that any of this means the event itself wasn't a genuinely worthwhile undertaking. Bowie makes his fans happy and I made them happy by putting their idol in cinemas around the world, where they could even talk to him directly (excluding a few cities I do concede!) That Australian fan was probably being a little too utopian when complaining about having to pay $15 for entry; few people argued it wasn't a bargain, although his larger question about how the technology was going to be used continued to haunt me. All along I thought my career was a benign, blossoming flower when really it was more like a wild, stampeding triffid! If I could write something that expressed this and not feel like a dollar hugging mercenary at the end of it maybe I'd be rid of the fever after all.

But would I? How many times in the book would I refer to mobile telephones as cell phones with a subliminal eye on the lucrative America market, where they don't refer to them as mobiles? And would I catch myself calling a holiday a vacation and be willing to change it back? Or would I swing back and forth between the cultural lingo, indicative of how I was still swinging back and forth between the remnants of fever and the salvation of recovery? I made a mental note to count the use of American phraseology once the book was published to see how often I lurched.

Nevertheless there was hope for me yet because art, like love, will take anyone back. Even the failed artist and notorious dictator Adolf Hitler, if he had reached for his old easel and paint sticks in the dying days of WW2, might have found something in his heart far less monstrous than what had been perpetrated during that most tragic of the 20th century's corporate showdowns. Art comes from a place that sin cannot touch. I relied on it to make me good again and started to write.

Meanwhile Terra Firma did ask around about me but there was never any chance of being resurrected at Odeon or UCI, as a spurning email made clear some weeks after the meeting. I'll never understand what those two little princes at Odeon had against me but I never stood a chance against them. How I wanted to give them a tactical thrashing! Power never lets go of a man lightly.

But I hold nothing against them anymore. For them film was *king*. And even when a king is dying, when his reign enters the inevitable transition stage, the monarchical realm finds favour with loyalists who will nonetheless defend it as staunchly as when it was at its peak. There was an analogous value to it that I could never have seen at the time.

There really was no way back into the industry, despite my illustrious track record. In several, fruitless attempts to clinch a business development post elsewhere I found that none of the other major cinema chains had much of an appetite for alternative programming. Like Odeon they were far too entrenched in films, what they called their "core business", to really give it a chance. Richard Segal was unique.

Yes, even then, knowing how ambition can eat you up without a fang being felt, I still wanted to keep my hat in the digital cinema ring, not least because I needed a day job to support the writing of a book and I didn't want to go back to temp work. It was flirting with disaster, of course, since there was no guarantee I wouldn't get sucked back into the rat race. But by then digital cinema was my speciality, something I was skilled in and I thought I could handle it.

So what would I have done if I'd stayed in the digital cinema business with a restored sense of balance? What potential might I suggest is being neglected as the technology continues its ascendancy? Well, there are possibilities for education worth considering. Not the unenlightened factory belt stuff that's hardwired into us during our school years but something that speaks to the adult rather than the adolescent, something that addresses the condition of being human rather than programming us to serve purely economic ends.

And possibly something that Australian fan said on the web about creating a sense of global unity the likes of which we haven't known before could be viable too. The cinema, after all, is the only place left where total strangers in every town and city in the world come together for a personal and social experience which actually offers some sense of belonging to a *community*. Institutional religion struggles in this regard, dividing people instead of uniting them, and its misread symbolisms block its power anyway.

But the cinema is a unique social zone that has stood the test of time and doesn't care what faith or race you belong to. From early childhood to old age we go there, opening up emotionally and psychologically in ways that no other medium can quite evoke. If we're ever going to forge a sense of belonging to a world community, maybe sharing a live, interactive experience of some kind with people in digital cinemas all around the world is not a bad place to start.

What might the uncannily accurate future-teller H. G. Wells have thought and predicted about digital cinema? The year 2004 actually saw a growing trend of socially and politically minded documentaries reach the cinema screen which, although not dependent on digital technology to do so, bodes well for experimenting with an increasing range of daring, progressive non-fiction in cinemas as the digital transition moves into its permanency. Wells might have said this was the best hope for the medium, although he may have added a note of caution.

When the documentary movies of Michael Moore came along, for example, I was just starting to take an interest in politics again and, like a lot of people, I thought finally here was a man blowing the lid off the corrupt political system with shining white honesty. But how wrong I was! Instead I saw the "left" of the political spectrum basically bashing the "right" instead of *both* sides being exposed for what they are.

The Left and Right of politics are easy to grasp. The Left want to limit rampant capitalism and control industry and commerce within a tightly regulated system; managed by a specialised class of intellectuals. It's still capitalism except it's what history has referred to as "state capitalism", where a limited number of shareholders in a centralised bureaucracy own the wealth of the land instead of enterprising individuals and businesses.

The Right, on the other hand, want markets left virtually wide open for every capitalist under the sun to freely compete; with society managed by a political class that they pick and fund. The Left use politicians too, to the extent that they have to, but the intellectual core like to reign supreme. Whichever system we get one set of capitalists or another comes out on top. Although on the Left they don't like to be called *capitalists* since it detracts from their derisory criticisms of the term. They prefer to be called *socialists*.

But in truth they are one and the same. All capitalists want to annihilate the competition, figuratively and sometimes literally, and dominate the marketplace. This puts the capitalist on a natural, evolutionary pathway to Leftism – except he needs the competitive system of Rightism to build a business in the first place.

Meanwhile both camps battle it out for overall supremacy, with the scales tipping back and forth. At best both sides co-exist in an uneasy peace, as with the 20th century's famously tense Cold War between the Rightist USA and the Leftist USSR. At worst we have cataclysmic disputes which engulf the whole world.

Nevertheless, a lot of people do actually buy into the arguments for why having a *few* capitalists running society under a form of central management is better than a *lot* of capitalists running around making up their own rules and vice versa.

The Leftist system has more cosmetic appeal than the Rightist system, of course. Ever since the Industrial Revolution the idea of containing the never-ending swell of greedy, rampant profiteers has resonated with a lot of ordinary people. That's been the problem – the Left's nobleness easily deceives. In power all men are finally equal – equal in their *weakness* to it.

And along the way no shortage of benign utopians and willing propagandists alike get drawn into the debate with moviemakers like the avowed Left-winger Michael Moore becoming popular, not by showing how both sides are equally self-serving and actually two aspects of the same thing, but by helping one set of capitalists either retain their position or expand it. Everyone thinks they are doing the right thing.

Some might say let's just tear down both the Left and the Right and start again. But that's anarchy. It won't work. The systems are too deeply entrenched. Basically you have to pick a side and try to reform it, either on the outside as a commentator of some kind or inside as a politician. Or at least you'll try to be a reformer until the whiff of power gets you and then you become what you thought you were reforming. H. G. Wells might have said that the problem isn't one of Left or Right but of *us* and *them*.

The Leftist surge of political critiques hitting cinemas at the start of the 21st century didn't stop with Moore. Rupert Murdoch's Rightist sympathies took a particularly acerbic bashing in a movie by a director named Robert Greenwald called *Outfoxed,* which threw mud at the media baron's Fox News Channel in the US, claiming it was a 24–hour propaganda machine for the American Republican Party.

I watched the Fox New Channel for a few weeks, since it is also broadcast on Murdoch's UK Sky satellite TV platform, and found that Greenwald was right. The Fox News Channel is indeed a biased, Right-wing mouthpiece but guess what? Greenwald's movie was backed by open supporters of the opposition Democratic Party, who would no doubt love to have a news channel like Fox to spread Leftist propaganda instead!

The other, major Leftist documentary of 2004 was *The Corporation* directed by Mark Achbar, based on the book *The Corporation: The Pathological Pursuit of Profit and Power* by Joel Bakan, which wheeled out a roster of Lefty lecture hall favourites to warn everyone about how rampant capitalism is ruining the world. It was another faithful hymn sheet rendition from the socialists that if just one or two of their own corporate sponsors were in charge, instead of dozens of the bastards, the new elite would of course be benign, perfect and make the world a better place. It seems hypocrisy is a trend that never goes out of fashion.

I think Wells – who became so alarmed at the direction politics was taking in the early 20th century that he even retired from writing fantasy novels at the peak of his career to concentrate on writing social and political discourses – would have walked out of these movies, fretting about those still glued to the screen and swallowing it all. I think he would have predicted that the most powerful and influential medium ever invented would have entered the digital age all too vulnerable to succumbing to the illusions and fantasy that the four walls of a movie theatre were originally intended for. But he might have championed its potential to truly bring people together and do something altruistically educational.

"History is more and more a race between education and catastrophe," the visionary novelist once said, demonstrating wisdom beyond his questionable free-loving ideology.

And there's something about the 3D experience that could have potential as well. 3D came along long before digital technology, first appearing as far back as the 1950s, but previously the format had been expensive to shoot properly and very complex to display, requiring two 35mm film projectors running simultaneously. Digital cinema changes all that. A single digital projector can now run full HD quality 3D from a single server without any of the alignment difficulties of running twin film projectors. Anyone who's seen a three dimensional movie in a cinema knows how amazing and immersive the experience is. We're limited only by our imaginations in how far we could go with it.

Who knows if I would have tried going down any of those paths if a cinema chain somewhere had been prepared to trial me for six months, as I went around proposing. I certainly wasn't thinking in those terms when Odeon fired me. I just wanted to get back in the business. Revolutions were on hold and might have stayed there. But it wasn't to be, and I was dropped irretrievably in the recycle bin along with all those other well-heeled hotshots from the likes of Boeing and Technicolor. I may have outlived them but not for long. I could always have tried something as an independent of course, but I thought maybe the real way back to me was through the pen.

I did pick up the occasional project management gig via Carlton Screen Advertising, however, who continued to show initiative with digital projects even after my disappearance from the scene. One of their young, bright account directors, James Dobbin, would regularly hire me to organise DVD screenings at various cinemas around the country, sponsored by numerous clients, and although these were small scale jobs it kept some money coming in, which meant I didn't have to get a typical nine-to-five.

At the same time I couldn't help but keep my eyes on who was doing what in digital cinema. The American music star Prince was the next big artist to experiment with the concept, launching his *Musicology* concert tour with a special performance on March 29th 2004 at the Staples Center in Los Angeles which was beamed live via satellite to around 40 theatres in the US, all of them Regal. Dolby managed to win the coveted 5.1 digital sound kudos, and their rivalry with DTS continues.

When I found out about the Prince gig I tried doing a last minute deal with Regal to downlink it at Odeon Leicester Square, since at the time I was still very much an Odeon man. But it didn't happen and as far as I know the show played to US audiences only. To date nobody has tried staging anything close to the scale of the Bowie gig. Eventually somebody will, and they may even go bigger. The technology knows no bounds.

And, as Robert Young had forecast, DTS did indeed spread their wings into Quantum Digital territory. And they bagged a Bob Geldof project no less! In early November 2004 the celebrated Live Aid concert from July 1985 was released as a special DVD box set and, on November 12th, DTS organised digital screenings of a specially edited version at multiple cinemas across the UK and Europe. It was a marketing ploy for the DVD as well as a profile building exercise for DTS in their new guise as a systems provider handling content management in general and not just sound. They hadn't even got me a ticket for it.

Thankfully the bitterness and bile I had felt eroding my spiritual centre ever since Disney's Phil Barlow had got in my face three years earlier was less present now and I just let DTS get on with it. At least I was being mown over by people I genuinely liked! And the ease of my forgiveness at least meant I was genuinely finding my spirituality again after so much anger and deviousness had cluttered up my psyche.

The renewal of my spirituality was in no small way benefited by the fact that I had already found it once in my life. Many people are lost to the corporate ladder without having experienced a glimpse of their spirit in the first place. These are the hardest people to reach because they have no sense of anything to come back to. Believing in any kind of spiritual revolution became more daunting once I realised this.

I could never have imagined how powerful the forces of self-interest would prove, to the extent that not even the person afflicted by them can see what's happening. All bad men think they are good, without exception. I would have been naïve in the extreme to have set out three years earlier thinking I could show a movie, make a few speeches and win converts. Even if I had got somewhere it is very probable that a similar power quest would have gripped me at some stage and, instead of plotting against those two little princes at Odeon and disposing of the likes of BT and SBE, I might have been scheming for an altogether different realm of power.

I wish I could tell you my "rediscovery of self" at the end of 2004 meant I was back with a vengeance to pick up where I left off and that the book I started was intended to serve as a platform the way *Jesus the Curry King* did back in 2000. But that's not the case. It's not the case because I cannot be entirely sure I won't slip back to being that dreadful, power-crazed eel I was before. It's not the case because the lure of power and self-interest has claimed too many of us already and I'm not sure we can get them back, especially those who never knew their soul in the first place. And finally it's not the case because there's just not enough time in one life to do it. I saw that the revolution is impossible.

As the stardust settled and I cocooned myself in the memories and realisation of all this I found myself challenged to be as honest as possible about what can happen to a man – even a man with spiritual and political convictions as deep as you now know mine were – when the world tempts us down the temporal, cheaply bejewelled road of self-interest. When it does we usually grab it and can find all the reasons in the world why we must.

And even as I proceeded to write I didn't know whether the tireless temptation to think commercially would claim the prose or whether I'd somehow do it better justice. Even now at the end I still don't know. You have to be the judge. Whichever verdict you deliver can only be a statement on the truth about the *reality* of being human. Even if I do win a favourable verdict there is still no certainty about the future. Have I disconnected the Voice for good or is it simply on permanent standby? Will I ignore my instincts again even when I know a person never should?

I don't really talk to Robert Young much any more. We would have made one heck of a team but he always said we were four or five years too early for digital cinema anyway. In a way he was right. As I was finishing this book in the summer of 2005 the number of DLP Cinema™ digital projector installations worldwide was still only around the 350 mark. When you consider that there are approximately 135,000 cinema screens worldwide it puts it into context. And with, approximately, only 100 studio titles released in digital format from January 1999 to August 2005, out of an average of the nearly 500 Hollywood movies released *each year*, it's no surprise the rollout has not been quicker. The high price of HD digital projectors, around $150K, has inevitably also been a factor. Film projectors typically cost under $50K.

Hollywood did at least set up a cross-studio focus group in March of 2002 called Digital Cinema Initiatives, LLC, otherwise known as DCI, to study the issues and make technical recommendations, which involved Disney, Fox, MGM, Paramount, Sony Pictures Entertainment, Universal and Warner

Bros. When I met the President of DCI, Chuck Goldwater, at the Cinema Expo trade show in 2004 – shortly before meeting UCI for that ill-fated contract discussion – I asked him how Hollywood's accountants and executives expected to advance digital cinema without first having the majority of their producers and directors wholly signed up to the image quality and security against piracy?

"Surely the artists have to buy into it, if it's going to happen," I had said. "At the moment everything is being led by the manufacturers, kind of the wrong way around isn't it?"

Goldwater acknowledged the point and was pleasant enough, but treated the meeting more like a press interview where he had to be politically delicate rather than free with his thoughts, which I could quite understand considering that he was appointed by the studio consortium to act as a sort of intermediary and wasn't actually the string puller himself.

Meanwhile in Europe a few independent initiatives have made better progress. In November 2004 a project called CinemaNet was launched, which involved digitally equipping over 100 cinema screens across eight countries for the exclusive purpose of screening documentary films on a monthly basis. The rollout was primarily funded by the EU MEDIA Programme and included the UK, Austria, Belgium, France, Germany, Holland, Slovakia and Spain. I haven't seen any of these documentaries yet and have no idea if the propaganda dial is routinely flying off the meter. Maybe I'll go and see one and keep my fingers crossed. The hi-tech gods, for all their potential, can be used to various ends, of course.

An even more ambitious rollout was announced in Ireland early in 2005 when the Irish Film Board declared that agreements with venture capitalists and technology partners had been reached to fully digitise all 515 Irish cinema screens with HD systems, suitable for Hollywood product as well as local movies that the Irish Film Board intends to support. The Irish Film Board's British equivalent, the invidious UK Film Council, also announced plans for a digital rollout during 2005, with around 200 cinemas across Britain, including several

Odeon and UCI sites, being named in a network costing close to
$20m of public money – although the UKFC intends to
distribute primarily sub-titled European movies out of the belief
that the British public wants to see more foreign-language films
at the local multiplex.

Gifted young directors coming off council estates in the likes
of Brixton and Newcastle can only hope that the UKFC rollout
is good news for them. What a great shame it will be if the
privileged ranks that have typically controlled film production
and distribution in the UK somehow get a monopoly on digital
distribution as well. We need all the artists we can get, after all.
Then again, I had my chance to create what I used to call a
"digital democracy" and I blew it, so maybe I have no right to
bash the toffs.

The biggest rollout of all so far looks set to be in China where,
by the end of this decade, some 2500 theatres are expected to get
the digital upgrade. India and Singapore are making bigger and
bigger strides as well. So even in the space of just twelve months
the numbers can change dramatically and in less than fifteen
years celluloid will probably exist only in art house theatres,
where cinema buffs can go to enjoy the nostalgia of a bygone
era, complete with paper posters in glass frames outside instead
of the electronic billboard signage we are gradually moving
toward. By then the dominance of Hollywood will likely have
passed its peak as more and more local, cultural programming
emerges. Who can say if it will be all about making money or if
something more profound comes of it? We'll have to see.

It all leaves me cautiously entering the publishing world,
having set up my own independent publishing company to
produce and market the material you're holding in your hand.
Once I've got it out there in the mainstream, in shops and
online, I don't really know what I'll do next. If a lot of you read
this book and make me a bestseller who knows what it'll do to
me. I've already shown I can't handle the air up there!

Maybe you should resell this book on Amazon or eBay so
that I don't profit from the next customer who buys it. And then
if they sell it on in the same way I'll be stuck seeing dwindling
returns on a book that ironically is being widely circulated. That

should keep me financially modest and away from craving a new empire in the book publishing business, shouldn't it? What a test of character that would be, to see if I minded. By all means try me.

I'll keep trying with love, though, and I still believe there's something there. Ivonne moved to England at the end of her contract and lives in Aylesbury now, just around the corner from me in a nice, little flat that she affords by working locally as a nursery nurse. From our kitchen windows we can wave to each other, across a distance of no more than forty metres, and I think we're in love.

But I still haven't completely figured love out yet, even after all this. I thought by now I'd have an uplifting, perfect picture of love to end on but that's not always the way it goes. Maybe love is something we can only understand over the course of an entire lifetime, picking up bits along the way from person to person, and everyone's mad expecting to figure it out like last week's crossword puzzle.

"I think it's a personal thing," Joanne said one day when I asked. "What it really means is probably going to be a little bit different for everyone."

I don't know if H. G. Wells was right to love the way he did but I know I'll always love Joanne, just as a friend of course. It seems love comes in all shapes and sizes, just like the fallible mortals it inhabits. The only thing I know about love for certain is that you cannot love anyone without a love for yourself, a love for who and what you are. Maybe that's why I couldn't love properly when ambition came calling. Deep down I knew it was a man I couldn't love. I think I'm ready to try loving again now.

If it all goes to hell with Ivonne maybe I'll go backpacking around Europe and catch up with how citizens feel about that persistent EU project – itself a classic, modern example of how the Left and the Right often do battle within the same geopolitical sphere. At the same time maybe I can figure out which of the Left or Right offers the best hope for any wide-eyed reformers. Bless them all. While I'm at it maybe I'll find love on the road. I won't ever give up on love, that's for sure. And if we're so damned determined to fight and kill each other I know that love is probably the only thing worth dying for.

Indeed, it even persuades me to reconsider fighting hopeless causes because, with love, you have something worth living for, even if we're doomed and the revolution is impossible. To live in a world where we can love what we are and properly love others – rather than know, deep down, that we were beaten by our flaws – has to be a place worth trying to find.

There really is a battle raging between the forces of Good and Evil for the soul and destiny of Mankind. But when we finally, truly come face to face with the enemy he will not be found on some distant battlefield or even in the corridors of power in Brussels or Washington. The enemy is *within*. It is in the nature of our being to wrestle with what is right and wrong and you have to stay very aware of which side is winning, no matter who you are or what principles you think you hold. Question yourself. Do it often. In the final analysis it wouldn't even be correct to say that the problem of Right and Left is a matter of *us* and *them* when really it's a matter of *us* and *us*.

But as least I've got a sense of my spirituality back now – if only I can hold onto it this time. But what exactly *is* spirituality and what can it do for you? Well, if I can get out of this blighted place having left just one story that encourages people to decipher the metaphorical references embedded in all the great spiritual texts, as well as in great art; which in turn bestows a consciousness that is then each person's mighty challenge to maintain, whilst having spun a tale with a few metaphors of my own – some obvious and some cryptic – that upholds the tradition yet applies to the times, I will have spoken my own, humble interpretation of the eternal language as best I could.

I've told the whole story now and it's time to let it go. If I need reminding of the experience I've just shared I can always look up at those satellites and remember how that broadcast spanned the world. Even if I can't see those hi-tech gods I know they are there. Or, at least, they are there for a while, until the orbit ends, until the final transmission is made and the electrical hum starts to fade as their marvellous circuits are put out of service. And then it's a trip among the stars for the former earth gazers.

Released from the monotony of seeing the world every day they can look forward to drifting off toward other worlds now, wondrous places that have been waiting for them to arrive, that have gotten used to seeing them on the cosmic horizon.

The decommissioned transmitters might look back for just a moment, as though remembering nostalgically what they left behind, angling to one side to catch a glimpse of the shiny blue ball with the sun poking up from just behind it. And somewhere among the heavens Tolstoy might cry "see, no matter how far you drift there's always a glimpse of light!"

And then as the satellites would pass slowly over the moon they might notice a tattered, old flag long since planted from the time of Man's first steps on its surface. How strange it would seem to them that men pledged allegiances to different parts of the planet considering the altogether different set of colours that the satellite brethren had served, the colours of the earth itself.